Wonders

Reader's Corner

IMAGINATION
An Odyssey Through Language

Wonders
Reader's Corner

Gail Heald-Taylor
General Consultant, Language Arts

HARCOURT BRACE JOVANOVICH, PUBLISHERS

Orlando   San Diego   Chicago   Dallas

Acknowledgments

For permission to reprint copyrighted material, grateful acknowledgment is made to the following sources:

Addison-Wesley Publishing Company, Reading, MA: "I Am Rose" from *The World Is Round* by Gertrude Stein. © 1966 by Addison-Wesley Publishing Company, Inc.

Atheneum Publishers, Inc.: Illustration from "The Fly in the Rye" and text and illustrations from "'Let's Marry!' Said the Cherry" in *Let's Marry Said the Cherry and Other Nonsense Poems* by N. M. Bodecker. Copyright © 1974 by N. M. Bodecker. A Margaret K. McElderry Book.

Harold Courlander and George Herzog: "Talk" from *The Cow-Tail Switch and Other West African Stories* by Harold Courlander and George Herzog. © 1947, 1975 by Holt, Rinehart and Winston; © 1981 by Harold Courlander and George Herzog.

Delacorte Press: From *Panda* by Susan Bonners. Copyright © 1978 by Susan Bonners.

Doubleday Publishing, a division of Bantam, Doubleday, Dell Publishing Group, Inc.: "I Go Forth to Move About the Earth" by Alonzo Lopez from *The Whispering Wind,* edited by Terry Allen. Copyright © 1972 by Institute of American Indian Arts.

Evil Eye Music, Inc., New York, NY: "Not Me" by Shel Silverstein. Copyright © 1968 by Evil Eye Music, Inc. Originally published in *Playboy* magazine, December 1960.

Miriam Farber, on behalf of the heirs of Norma Farber: "Spendthrift" by Norma Farber. © 1976 by Norma Farber.

Robert Froman: "Winter Walk" from *Street Poems* by Robert Froman. Copyright © 1971 by Robert Froman.

Patrick J. Gallagher: Mississippi Possum by Miska Miles.

Grosset & Dunlap, Inc.: "A very fat snowman . . ." from *The Big Book of Limericks* by Edward Mullins. Copyright © 1968 by Edward S. Mullins.

Harcourt Brace Jovanovich, Inc.: From *Rufus M* by Eleanor Estes. Copyright 1943, 1971 by Eleanor Estes. Abridged and adapted from "The Big Wind of '34" in *Grandpa's Farm* by James Flora. Copyright © 1965 by James Flora. "Theme in Yellow" from *Chicago Poems* by Carl Sandburg. Copyright 1916 by Holt, Rinehart and Winston, Inc., renewed 1944 by Carl Sandburg.

Harper & Row, Publishers, Inc. Adapted from *Wolfie* by Janet Chenery. Text copyright © 1969 by Janet Dai Chenery. "Spring" from *Dogs & Dragons, Trees & Dreams: A Collection of Poems* by Karla Kuskin. Copyright © 1968 by Karla Kuskin. "Gently, gently . . ." from *I See the Winds* by Kazue Mizumura. Copyright © 1966 by Kazue Mizumura. Published by Thomas Y. Crowell. Adapted from *Sparrow Socks* by George Selden. Text copyright © 1965 by George S. Thompson. Illustration from *Stevie* by John Steptoe. Copyright © 1969 by John L. Steptoe.

Barbara Shook Hazen: Adapted from *Amelia's Flying Machine* (Retitled: "Amelia's Roller Coaster") by Barbara Shook Hazen. Copyright © 1977 by Barbara Shook Hazen.

Houghton Mifflin Company and Allen & Unwin (Publishers) Ltd.: From "Oliphaunt" in *The Adventures of Tom Bombadil* by J. R. R. Tolkien. Copyright © 1962 by George Allen & Unwin Ltd.

Alfred A. Knopf, Inc.: "In Time of Silver Rain" from *Selected Poems of Langston Hughes* by Langston Hughes. Copyright 1938, renewed 1966 by Langston Hughes. From *The Cat Came Back* by Dahlov Ipcar. Copyright © 1971 by Dahlov Ipcar.

Ray Lincoln Literary Agency, 4 Surrey Road, Melrose Park, PA 19126: "Eat-It-All Elaine" from *Don't Ever Cross a Crocodile* by Kaye Starbird. Copyright © 1963 by Kaye Starbird. Published by J. B. Lippincott Company.

Little, Brown and Company: "The Grasshopper" from *One at a Time* by David McCord. Copyright 1952 by David McCord. From "Adventures of Isabel" in *Many Long Years Ago* by Ogden Nash. Copyright 1936 by Ogden Nash.

Macmillan Publishing Company: From *The Tales of Olga da Polga* by Michael Bond. Copyright © 1971 by Michael Bond. "March" from *Summer Green* by Elizabeth Coatsworth. Copyright 1948 by Macmillan Publishing Company, renewed 1976 by Elizabeth Coatsworth Beston. From "Something Told the Wild

Geese" in *Poems* by Rachel Field. Copyright 1934 by Macmillan Publishing Company, renewed 1962 by Arthur S. Pederson.

Macmillan Publishing Company and Macmillan, London and Basingstoke: "Paper Boats" from *The Crescent Moon* in *Collected Poems and Plays* by Rabindranath Tagore. Copyright 1913 by Macmillan Publishing Company, renewed 1941 by Rabindranath Tagore.

McIntosh and Otis, Inc.: Just the Thing for Geraldine by Ellen Conford. Text copyright © 1974 by Ellen Conford.

Philomel Books: Adapted text and illustrations from *The Emperor and the Kite* by Jane Yolen, illustrated by Ed Young. Text copyright © 1967 by Jane Yolen; illustrations copyright © 1967 by World Publishing Company.

G. P. Putnam's Sons: "The Beach" from *The Adventures of Mole and Troll* by Tony Johnston, illustrated by Wallace Tripp. Text copyright © 1972 by Tony Johnston; illustrations copyright © 1972 by Wallace Tripp.

Marian Reiner: "Winter Night" from *The Golden Hive,* poems and pictures by Harry Behn. Copyright © 1957, 1962, 1966 by Harry Behn. All rights reserved.

Marian Reiner, on behalf of Myra Cohn Livingston: "Discovery" from *Whispers and Other Poems* by Myra Cohn Livingston. © 1958 by Myra Cohn Livingston. "The Fourth of July" by Myra Cohn Livingston. Copyright © 1986 by Myra Cohn Livingston.

Charles Scribner's Sons, a division of Macmillan, Inc.: Adapted from *Guess Who My Favorite Person Is* by Byrd Baylor. Copyright © 1977 by Byrd Baylor.

Sally Andresen Stolte: "Fall" by Sally Andresen. Originally published in *The Student Writer.*

Viking Penguin Inc.: Adapted from *Dance of the Animals,* retold by Pura Belpré. Copyright © 1972 by Pura Belpré White. From *Along Sandy Trails,* text by Ann Nolan Clark, photographs by Alfred A. Cohn. Text copyright © 1969 by Ann Nolan Clark; photographs copyright © 1969 by Alfred A. Cohn.

Art Acknowledgments

Jane Barton: 25; Willi K. Baum: 283; Chuck Bowden: 102, 202, 254, 280 (adapted from photographs from the following sources: 102, courtesy UPI; 202, courtesy Harcourt Brace Jovanovich, Inc.; 254, courtesy Pura Belpré); Bert Dodson: 102–103; Alyce Gatchell: 116, 180, 186, 346; Sharon Harker: 26, 27, 229; Marlies Najaka: 160–178; Stephanie Pershing: 58, 132, 142, 314, 388, 394; Francisco Rodriguez: 204, 218, 378; Ed Taber: 282, 283, 284.

Cover: Tom Vroman

Maps: Joanna Adamska Koperska

Unit Openers: Jane Teiko Oka

Production and Layout: Intergraphics

Contents

4 You Can't Catch Me

1 One of a Kind

TALKING ABOUT THE THEME

Look at the picture on page 1. Read the title.

1. What is everyone watching in the picture?

2. How is the clown one of a kind?

3. How do you think the people and the animals in the picture feel? Why do you think as you do?

4. Is it easy or hard to make people laugh? Tell why you think as you do.

5. You will read some selections. How do you think the selections will be alike?

Other Books About One-of-a-Kind Things

Do Not Open by Brinton Turkle. E. P. Dutton, 1981. A creature released from a bottle found on the beach leads Miss Moody and her cat, Captain Kidd, on merry adventures.

Charlotte's Web by E. B. White. Harper & Row, 1980. A spider who spins messages in webs and a young girl save the life of Wilbur the pig.

Focusing on "The Beach"

▶ Write down everything you know about beaches. Discuss your ideas with your classmates. Ask questions about their ideas.

▶ Look at the picture on page 4. Think about what you discussed about beaches.
  • Do you think Mole and Troll are enjoying themselves? How do you know?
  • What might happen in this story?

▶ Get ready to read a play about two friends, Mole and Troll. As you read, think about what happens to them. Think about how to fill in this chart.

Mole and Troll	
What Happens	What They Do

Now turn the page and read "The Beach."
Then you will talk about misunderstandings.

The Beach

A play adapted from the story by Tony Johnston
Pictures by Wallace Tripp

Characters

Storyteller 1   **Storyteller 2**   **Mole**   **Troll**

Storyteller 1: Mole and Troll went to the beach.
They felt the warm sand
between their toes.

Storyteller 2: They felt the warm sun on their backs.
When it got too hot,
they sat by the tide pools
and dangled their toes in the water.

Storyteller 1: Suddenly, Mole jumped up!

Mole: You pinched me!

Troll: I did not!
I was sitting here dangling my toes
and minding my own business.

Mole: Well, maybe your business is pinching.
There is no one else around.

Storyteller 2: Troll made a face. He did not like being called a pincher.
No one said anything for a little while.

Storyteller 1: Then Troll felt a pinch on his toe.

Troll: OU-OU-CH! Stop that pinching, Mole.
Just because someone pinches you,
you do not have to pinch me!

Mole: I did not touch you!

Troll: You did! You did! You *did!*
There is no one else around.

Mole: Look, Troll, it is too nice a day
for arguing.
Let's enjoy the sea
and forget this silliness.

Storyteller 2: So they sat and enjoyed the sea.
The salt mist touched them and felt cool.
Sea gulls flew by,
and everything was calm.

Storyteller 1: Then Mole cried out.

Mole: YI-I-IKES!
You did it again, you fuzzy troll!

Storyteller 2: Troll felt a pinch, too.

Troll: It was you!
This time you pinched me so hard,
you made a little red lump. Look!

Storyteller 1: Mole leaned over to look
and there was a little red lump.

Mole: I did not do that. You have a hive.

Troll: How can I have just one hive?
Hives come in bunches!

Mole: I don't know! But you do!

Troll: All right, we will sit very still
with our hands on our heads
and *see* which one is pinching.

Mole: You are sneaky,
because then you will pinch
with your feet.

Troll: Then we will sit very still
with our hands on our heads
and our feet in plain sight.

Mole: Okay, Troll. We will do that.
But I am sitting on seaweed
to protect myself on all sides.

Troll: Then so am I.

Storyteller 2: So they sat very still
on big seaweed piles
with their hands on their heads
and their feet in plain sight
to see who was pinching.
They sat like that for a long time.

Storyteller 1: At last Mole said,

Mole: Troll! It is too still.
Nothing is happening.
There is something funny about this.

Storyteller 2: Someone else thought it was funny, too.
Someone else giggled very loudly.

Storyteller 1: It was a big crab.
He had been doing the pinching.
They looked so silly
that he could not help giggling.
Mole and Troll chased him,
but he ran into a tight hole
and giggled for half an hour.

Troll: Mole, I am sorry for shouting at you.

Mole: Me, too. And I would never pinch you, because you are my friend.

Troll: Me, too.

Storyteller 2: Then they went swimming in a place where there were no crabs at all.

Think about the play. Copy the chart on page 3. Fill in the information. Then answer the questions.

1. Use your chart. What happens to Mole? How does Mole feel about what happens?

2. Use your chart. What happens to Troll? How does Troll's reaction compare with Mole's?

3. Why do you think Mole and Troll blame each other for what happened?

4. Suppose Mole and Troll had not discovered the crab. Would they have remained friends? Tell why you think as you do.

5. Why does this play belong in a unit about things that are one of a kind?

6. What else might have pinched Troll and Mole?

Talk about how friends settle misunderstandings. Ask questions about what your classmates say. Talk about the answers.

WORK IN A GROUP

Focusing on "'Let's Marry!' Said the Cherry"

Think and Read

▶ Talk about what you know about weddings. Ask questions to learn more.

▶ Look at the picture on page 17. Think about what you know about weddings.
  • Why do you think the pea is crying?
  • What might happen in this poem?

▶ Get ready to read a poem about some plants. As you read, think about the plans they make. Think about how to answer the questions in the chart.

Details in "'Let's Marry!' Said the Cherry"
Who is the bride? _____
Who is the groom? _____
What will the bride wear? _____
What will the guests wear? _____
Where will the wedding be? _____
Who is the preacher? _____

Now turn the page and read "'Let's Marry!' Said the Cherry." Then you will talk about some silly things.

"Let's Marry!" Said the Cherry

Poem and pictures by N. M. Bodecker

"Let's marry,"
said the cherry.

"Why me?"
said the pea.

"'Cause you're sweet,"
said the beet.

"Say you will,"
said the dill.

"Think it over,"
said the clover.

"Don't rush,"
said the squash.

"Here's your dress,"
said the cress.

"White and green,"
said the bean.

"And your cape,"
said the grape.

"Trimmed with fur,"
said the burr.

"Won't that tickle?"
said the pickle.

"Who knows?"
said the rose.

"Where's the chapel?"
said the apple.

"In Greenwich,"
said the spinach.

"We'll be there!"
said the pear.

"Wearing what?"
said the nut.

"Pants and coats,"
said the oats.

"Shoes and socks,"
said the phlox.

"Shirt and tie,"
said the rye.

"We'll look jolly,"
said the holly.

"You'll look silly,"
said the lily.

"You're crazy,"
said the daisy.

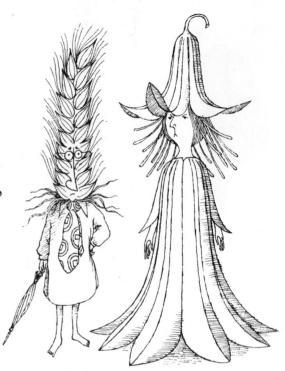

"Come, let's dine,"
said the vine.

"Yeah—let's eat!"
said the wheat.

"And get stout,"
said the sprout.

"Just wait,"
said the date.

"Who will chime?"
said the lime.

"I'll chime!"
said the thyme.

"Who will preach?"
said the peach.

"It's my turn!"
said the fern.

"You would ramble,"
said the bramble.

"Here they come!"
cried the plum.

"Start the tune!"
cried the prune.

"All together!"
cried the heather.

"Here we go!"
said the sloe.

"NOW—let's marry!"
said the cherry.

"Why me?"
said the pea.

"Oh, my gosh!"
said the squash.

22

"Start all over,"
said the clover.

"NO WAY!"
said the hay.

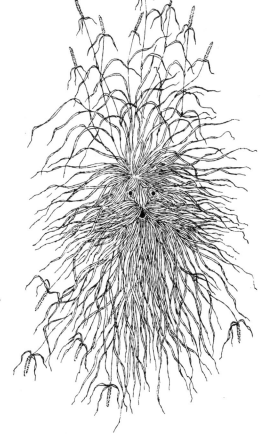

Think about the poem. Copy the chart on page 16. Fill in the information. Then answer the questions.

1. Use your chart. Who are the bride and groom? What do you think about this?

2. Use your chart. What do the plants in the poem do that real plants do not do?

3. Use your chart. Think about what you know about weddings. What do you think about the plants' wedding plans?

4. Suppose this poem did not rhyme. How would it be different?

5. What if this poem told about people instead of plants? Would this poem belong in a unit about things that are one of a kind? Tell why or why not.

6. Pretend you are a plant. Think of your plant name. Think of a rhyming couplet to add to the poem.

Talk about what makes something silly. Ask questions about what your classmates say. Talk about the answers.

WORK IN A GROUP

POETRY

Rhyming Couplets by Myra Cohn Livingston

When two things or two friends go together, you can call them a couple. In poetry, when two lines that rhyme go together, they are called a *rhyming couplet* (KUHP•lit). The sound that ends the first line is repeated in the second line. Rhyming couplets are fun to hear, and they are easy to remember.

Here are two rhyming couplets from the poem "'Let's Marry!' Said the Cherry" by N. M. Bodecker.

This is a rhyming couplet.

This is a rhyming couplet, too.

"Let's marry," said the cherry.

"Why me?" said the pea.

In the first couplet, the word that ends the first line is *marry.* It rhymes with *cherry,* the last word in the second line. What are the rhyming words in the second couplet?

Poets often use rhyming couplets in their poems. Some are long poems. Some are short. Gertrude Stein uses only two couplets in her poem "I Am Rose."

I am Rose my eyes are blue
I am Rose and who are you?
I am Rose and when I sing
I am Rose like anything.

Blue and *you* are the rhyming words in the first couplet. What are the rhyming words in the second couplet?

Rules for a Rhyming Couplet

1. Two lines must come one after the other.
2. The end words of both lines must rhyme.

Remember these rules!

27

Read these poems. Which ones have
rhyming couplets? What are the rhyming words?

1. **Discovery**

   Round and round and round I spin
   Making a circle so I can fall in.
   —Myra Cohn Livingston

2. A peanut sat on a railroad track,
   His heart was all a-flutter.
   The five-fifteen came rushing by—
   Toot! toot! peanut butter!
   —An American folk rhyme

3. "What's the news of the day,
   Good neighbor, I pray?"
   "They say the balloon
   Has gone up to the moon!"
   —An old rhyme

Try writing some rhyming couplets
yourself. Begin with two couplets. Then
perhaps you'll try writing a longer poem.

Focusing on "Just the Thing for Geraldine"

▶ Talk about the different kinds of lessons you might take. Ask your classmates questions.

▶ Look at the title on page 30 and the pictures on pages 30–39. Think about lessons you know about.
  - Who do you think is the main character?
  - What kind of lessons are being given? What makes you think as you do?
  - What might happen in this story?

▶ Get ready to read a story about a possum named Geraldine. As you read, think about what Geraldine is good at doing. Notice what she is not so good at doing. Think about what to add to this chart.

What Geraldine Is Good at Doing	What Geraldine Is Not So Good at Doing

Now turn the page and read "Just the Thing for Geraldine." Then you will talk about talents.

29

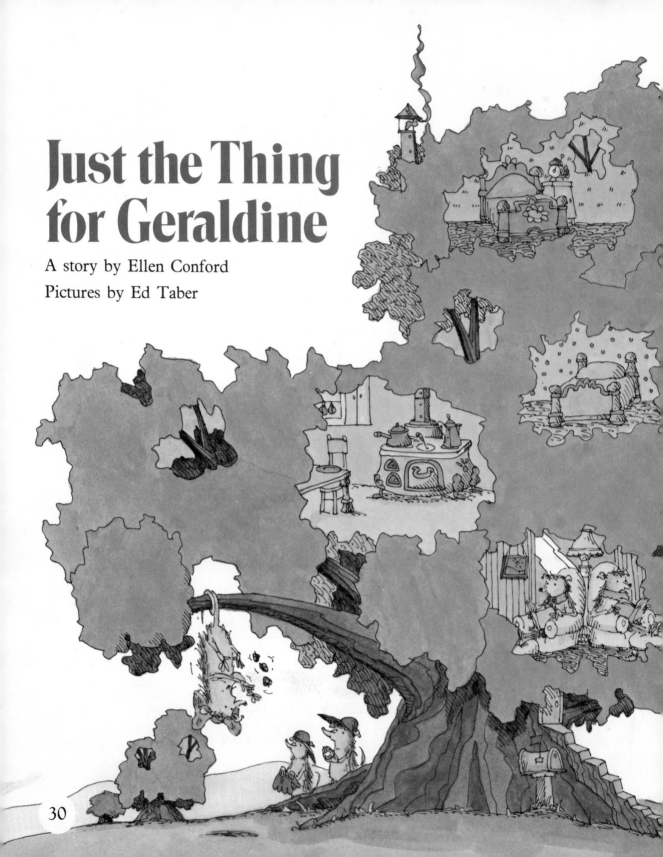

Just the Thing for Geraldine

A story by Ellen Conford

Pictures by Ed Taber

Geraldine the possum lives with her parents and her brothers Eugene and Randolph in a big, old tree. Geraldine can often be found there, hanging from a tree branch and juggling.

There was nothing Geraldine liked better than hanging by her tail from the branch of a tree and juggling a few acorns.

But her parents told her there was more to life than juggling, so every week she went to Mademoiselle La Fay's School of the Dance to learn ballet.

"It will help you to be graceful," said her mother.

"It will help you to be ladylike," said her father.

"It will help you keep physically fit," said her brother Randolph.

"Nothing could help her," whispered her brother Eugene.

One day Geraldine came home from ballet school very excited.

"Everybody come look!" she shouted. "Come look at what I can do!"

"What is it?" asked her mother.

"We learned the Dance of the Purple Swan," Geraldine said.

"That's wonderful!" said her mother.

"A whole dance!" exclaimed her father. "And you haven't even been going to dancing school very long."

"Swans aren't purple," said Eugene.

"Now, watch me," Geraldine ordered. "Are you looking?"

"We're looking," said her mother.

Geraldine smoothed down her tutu, which her mother had made for her out of leaves, and gracefully raised her forepaws over her head.

"Dee, da da da da dee ta dum," she hummed, and ran lightly, on tiptoe, around the trunk of the tree.

"Oh, how beautiful," sighed her mother.

"Encore, encore!" clapped her father.

"That's pretty good, Geraldine," said Randolph.

"Can we go play now?" asked Eugene.

"Dee, da da da da ta dum," Geraldine hummed, and began to dance faster around the tree.

But one of the big roots of the tree was sticking up from the ground and Geraldine didn't see it.

"Ow!" yelled Geraldine, as she tripped over the root and sprawled on the ground.

"Did you hurt yourself?" asked her
mother worriedly.

"No," Geraldine sniffled, and ran up
the tree before Randolph and Eugene could
see her tears. She hung upside down by her
tail, her leafy ballet skirt covering her face.

"I see you, Randolph," she said angrily.
"You think I can't see you, but I can.
You'd better stop laughing."

Randolph covered his mouth with his paw.

"I'm not laughing," he said, trying to
sound serious.

"Is it all right if *I* laugh?" asked Eugene.

"There is nothing to laugh at," their
father said sternly.

"Geraldine just tripped," their mother said. "It could happen to anyone."

"Especially Geraldine," whispered Eugene to Randolph.

"I heard you, Eugene!" Geraldine shouted. "You think I can't hear you, but I can!" She pulled herself back up on the branch and straightened her tutu. "I'd like to see *you* do the Dance of the Purple Swan."

"Swans aren't purple," said Eugene. "Swans are white."

Randolph and Eugene went back to their game. Geraldine took off her ballet skirt. She looked at it thoughtfully as she folded it and put it away.

The following week, when Geraldine came home from ballet school, her mother and father were waiting for her.

"Well, what did you learn at dancing school today?" her mother asked eagerly.

"I learned," Geraldine said unhappily, "that I am not a very good dancer."

"Nonsense!" said her father. "You dance beautifully. And you haven't even been going to dancing school very long."

"And I don't think I'll be going much longer," said Geraldine.

"Oh, of course you will," said her mother. "You'll see, you'll be a graceful dancer in no time."

Geraldine shook her head.

"No, I won't," she said. "I cannot do *pliés* and *arabesques*, and when we're supposed to dance on our toes my toes curl up and I fall down. I am just not cut out for ballet."

"But I thought you liked ballet school," said her mother.

"I like juggling better," said Geraldine.

"But don't you want to learn to be graceful?" asked her father.

"No," said Geraldine, swinging back and forth by her tail from the branch of the tree and juggling some pebbles. "Not really."

"Oh," said her mother.

So, her mother signed her up for a class at Schuyler's School of Sculpture.

"I'm sure you have artistic talent," said her mother.

"Sculpture school is just the thing for you, Geraldine," agreed her father.

"I don't know," said Geraldine, doubtfully, as she flipped three blackberries in the air and balanced a twig on the end of her nose.

"Oh, you'll see," said her mother. "You'll make bowls and pitchers and artistic statues. Sculpture school will be lots of fun."

Every week Geraldine went to Schuyler's School of Sculpture, and every week her parents asked, "How do you like sculpture school?"

And every week Geraldine shrugged and said, "It's okay, I guess."

One day Geraldine came home from class carrying a big pile of something wrapped in wet leaves.

"What's that?" asked Randolph.

"That's clay," said Geraldine.

"What's it for?" asked Eugene curiously.

"We have to make a sculpture of someone," Geraldine said.

"Oh, boy!" cried Eugene, jumping up and standing very straight and flexing his muscles. "Do me, Geraldine, do me!"

"We just have to do the head," Geraldine said.

"Oh," said Eugene, disappointed. "Well," he brightened a minute later, "do *my* head." He turned his head sideways so Geraldine could see his profile. "I have a nice head. Please, Geraldine?"

"You have to sit very still," Geraldine warned. "You can't move around or wiggle or anything."

"I won't," promised Eugene. "I won't even blink."

Geraldine sat Eugene down in front of her and turned his head sideways. She unwrapped the mound of clay and put it on a tree stump. Randolph sat down next to her.

"Don't sit there and watch me!" Geraldine snapped. "How do you expect me to concentrate when you're staring at me like that?"

"You're very touchy," said Randolph. "Why are you in such a bad mood?"

"I'm not in a bad mood!" yelled Geraldine. "Now, go away and leave me alone!"

Randolph went off to play ball and Geraldine began to work on her sculpture.

After a while, Eugene began to squirm.

"Is it finished yet, Geraldine?" he asked.

"No," said Geraldine.

"My nose itches," complained Eugene.

"Sit still and be quiet!" Geraldine ordered.

Geraldine molded the clay, squeezing it, poking it, and muttering to herself while she worked.

"What are you saying, Geraldine?"
Eugene asked. "I can't hear you."

"I'm saying 'stupid clay!'" Geraldine
snapped. "Now will you be still? How can
I sculpt you if you keep wriggling around?"

"I can't help it," Eugene whined. "I'm
getting tired. My neck hurts. And I think I
have to sneeze."

"Be quiet. And I'm doing your mouth
now, so please keep it shut."

Eugene sighed. Geraldine went on
molding and muttering.

Finally she said, "There. It's done. I
think."

"Oh, good!" said Eugene, jumping up and stretching. "I feel stiff all over. Let's see it."

But Geraldine was covering her sculpture with the wet leaves.

"Let me see it," Eugene said. "Why are you covering it up? I want to see my head."

He ran over to the tree stump and began pulling off the leaves.

"Stop it!" yelled Geraldine, swatting at him. "You stop that, Eugene! I don't want you to look at it. I don't want *anybody* to look at it."

"I won't hurt it," Eugene said, yanking off the leaves. "I want to see it."

Randolph and their mother and father came running when they heard Eugene and Geraldine.

"What's going on?" asked their father.

"Why are you two screaming like this?" asked their mother.

"*What* is *that?*" Randolph asked, pointing toward the tree stump.

Eugene had pulled all the leaves off Geraldine's sculpture and was backing away from the tree stump, shaking his head in fury.

"That is *not* me!" he howled. "I don't look like that!"

"Well, if you didn't move around so much—" Geraldine shouted.

"Is *that* supposed to be *Eugene?*" Randolph asked.

"It's . . . it's very interesting," their father said weakly.

"It is not interesting!" shrieked Eugene. "It's a bunch of lumps! I don't look like a bunch of lumps!"

Geraldine sighed, and began to cover up her sculpture with leaves again. When she finished covering it all up, she climbed the tree and hung by her tail, swinging gently back and forth as she juggled some pine cones.

A little while later Randolph and Eugene came up the tree and sat down next to Geraldine.

"You sure are a good juggler, Geraldine," said Randolph kindly.

"Thank you," Geraldine murmured.

Randolph gave Eugene a poke in the ribs.

"Ow! I mean, oh," said Eugene, "I wish I could juggle like you can."

"Do you really?" Geraldine asked.

"You're the best juggler we know. ISN'T THAT RIGHT, EUGENE?" said Randolph, glaring at his brother.

"Yes," Eugene said.

"So we'd like you to teach us how to juggle," Randolph said. "WOULDN'T WE, EUGENE?"

"Yes," Eugene said.

"Oh," said Geraldine, happily, "of course I'll teach you. It's not too hard, once you get the hang of it. Now, just watch me and—"

"Geraldine!" her mother called. "I've thought of just the thing for you!"

"What is it?" asked Geraldine.

"Singing lessons!" her mother said excitedly. "How would you like to take singing lessons?"

"No," said Geraldine, juggling her acorns.

"No?" her father asked. "But you'd love singing lessons."

"No," repeated Geraldine. "I wouldn't."

"But, why not, Geraldine?" asked her mother.

"What if I'm not a good singer?" said Geraldine. "I took ballet lessons and found out I wasn't a good dancer."

"And you certainly aren't good at sculpting," Eugene added.

"She sure is a good juggler, though," said Randolph. "And nobody ever gave her juggling lessons."

"That's true," their mother said.

"I never thought of that," said their father.

"Neither did I," said Geraldine.

Suddenly, she stopped juggling and jumped up.

"I'll be right back," she said, and ran down the tree.

In a little while, Geraldine returned. She was lugging a big piece of wood.

"What's that?" asked Randolph.

Geraldine propped the wood up against the trunk of the tree.

"Come and look," she said proudly.

The possums came down from the tree.

"I made a sign," said Geraldine.

"What kind of a sign?" asked Eugene. "What does it say?"

"Oh, it's beautiful," said their mother.

"Aren't you the clever one!" said their father.

"What does it *say?*" cried Eugene. "Tell me what it says!"

"It says," Randolph told him, "GERALDINE'S JUGGLING SCHOOL."

GERALDINE'S JUGGLING SCHOOL

Think about the story. Copy the chart on page 29. Fill in the information. Then answer the questions.

1. Use your chart. What is Geraldine not so good at doing? Why do you think this is so?

2. Why do you think Geraldine's parents want her to learn ballet and sculpture?

3. Why does Geraldine not want to take singing lessons?

4. Think about Geraldine's brother Randolph. What do you think his special talent might be? Tell why. Tell how you think he might use his talent.

5. Geraldine opens a juggling school. How else might she use her talent for juggling?

6. Why is this story in a unit about things that are one of a kind?

WORK IN A GROUP

Tell what having a talent means to you. Ask questions about what your classmates say. Talk about the answers.

Focusing on "Spiders Are Special"

Think and Read

▶ Talk about what you know about spiders. Ask your classmates questions.

▶ Look at the words in dark type on pages 52, 54, and 55. Think about what you know about spiders.

- What will this information story be about?
- Will what you read in this information story be true? How do you know?

▶ Get ready to read an information story about spiders. Think about how spiders catch food. Think about where spiders live. Copy this chart. Then fill in the facts as you read.

Spiders That Spin Webs	Spiders That Hunt	Spiders Everywhere!

Now turn the page and read "Spiders Are Special." Then you will talk about how spiders get their food.

51

Spiders Are Special

Spiders That Spin Webs

This web was made by a small garden spider. It is an *orb web* that is shaped like a wheel with many spokes. A web like this might be three feet across. Yet a small spider spun it in about an hour.

Sticky silk threads go around this web. Insects stick to them and are caught. The spider is careful to walk only on the dry, straight threads that go to the web's center. As it moves, the spider keeps coating its legs with oil. Then, if it touches a sticky thread, the spider does not get stuck.

Pictures by Joanna Adamska Koperska

The zigzag marks on the orb web are made of another kind of thread. They are made of thick, fuzzy silk. People have long wondered about these zigzag marks. Some scientists now believe that the zigzags act as a signal to birds. A web is hard to see, but birds can spot the zigzag marks when they fly. When they see the marks, the birds turn away. They do not fly into the web and tear it.

Spiders that spin webs do not see very well. They use webs to trap their food. Some spiders wait in their webs until an insect is trapped. When they feel the web move, they hurry out to get their meal. Other spiders stay in a hiding place. They spin a long thread out to the web. The thread is called a *dragline*. When the dragline moves, the spider knows an insect has been trapped.

Spiders That Hunt

Not all spiders spin webs to catch food. Some spiders are hunters. The jumping spider and the wolf spider both hunt their food.

Spiders that hunt have large eyes. They see much better than spiders that spin. Hunters see well enough to hunt for food. Just below the hunters' eyes are two strong, pointed teeth called *fangs*. Hunting spiders use their fangs to bite and kill insects.

Hunting spiders' bodies are often very hairy. Their legs are thick and powerful. Hunters use their legs in different ways to help them hunt for food. Jumping spiders jump on insects. Wolf spiders run fast enough to catch their food. Some hunting spiders just reach out and grab the insects they want to eat.

jumping spider

Spiders Everywhere!

Hunting and web-spinning spiders catch and eat millions of insects every year, so spiders live almost anywhere insects live. Spiders live in people's houses. Spiders live in fields and forests. They live in wet basements and dusty barns. They live in caves and swamps, and even underwater. Spiders live everywhere! Look for them. You may find some as small as this dot (•) or as big as this page. You may also find out for yourself what makes spiders so special.

This **crab spider,** a hunter, can change color. It turns pink, white, or yellow so it can't be seen hiding in flowers or leaves.

The **fishing spider** is a hunter that catches and eats small fish.

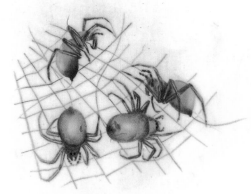

The **water spider** makes a bell-shaped web that holds a bubble of air. The spider lives, eats, and raises its young in the air bell.

Baby spiders sometimes travel through the air on silk threads.

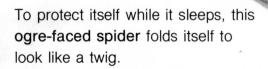

To protect itself while it sleeps, this **ogre-faced spider** folds itself to look like a twig.

The **ray spider** builds a special web that is pulled into an umbrella shape by one thread. When an insect flies in, the thread breaks. The web tangles around the spider's next meal.

Think about the selection. Look at the facts you wrote on your chart. Then answer the questions.

1. Use your chart. Also, think about what you know about spiders. How do spiders that spin webs get their food?

2. Use your chart. How do spiders that hunt get their food?

3. Do you think hunting or spinning a web is a better way for a spider to catch food? Tell why you think as you do.

4. Why do you think spiders can live anywhere?

5. How might spiders be helpful in a house, in a barn, or in a forest?

6. The title of this selection is "Spiders Are Special." Are they also one of a kind? Why or why not?

7. Suppose you were a web-spinning spider. Where would you spin your web? Why?

Tell how a spider might not get any food. Ask questions about what your classmate says. Talk about the answers.

58

Focusing on "Wolfie"

▶ Think about something that is important to you. Talk about how to take care of it. Ask your classmates questions.

▶ Look at the title and the pictures on pages 60–78. Think about what you know about taking care of things.
  • Who or what do you think Wolfie is? What makes you think as you do?
  • What might happen in this story?

▶ Get ready to read a story about three children and an unusual pet. As you read, think about what the children do and why. Think about how to finish this chart.

Main Characters	What They Do for Wolfie
1.	
2.	
3.	
4.	

Now turn the page and read "Wolfie." Then you will talk about caring for a pet.

Wolfie

A story by Janet Chenery

Pictures by Dan Siculan

Harry and George sat in their secret meeting place. It was a large doghouse for Harry's dog. But Biffy never used it, so Harry and George did.

"How many flies did you catch?" asked Harry.

"Three," said George. He pulled a small bottle out of his pocket.

"Only three?" asked Harry. "We will need more than that."

George sighed. "It took me an hour to catch these. Are you sure he likes flies?"

"Sure," said Harry. "Don't you remember? The book said that spiders eat live flies and other insects."

"Yes," said George. "But the spider in the picture had a web. Wolfie hasn't made a web yet."

"He will make a web when he sees the flies," Harry said. He picked up a big jar. Something inside it moved. "Hello, Wolfie," Harry whispered. He unscrewed the jar lid carefully. "Get ready," he told George.

George turned his bottle upside down over the big jar. He took off the bottle top and shook the flies into the jar.

Harry quickly put the lid back on. "Have a fly, Wolfie," said Harry.

They watched the brown spider in the jar. At first it did not move. Then it made a dash at the fly. But the fly got away just in time.

Outside the doghouse someone called, "Harry!"

"Shh! It's Polly," Harry whispered. "Hide Wolfie!"

Polly was Harry's little sister. "I want to see the spider," she said.

"No!" said Harry. "Go away! Scram!"

"Wait, Harry," George said. Then he stuck his head out of the doghouse. He said to Polly, "You can see Wolfie. But first you have to bring him a hundred flies. Live ones."

"Okay," said Polly, and off she ran.

"Why did you tell her that?" asked Harry. "Now she'll pester us all the time."

"No, she won't," said George. "It's very hard to catch flies."

"You don't know Polly," Harry grumbled.

They watched Wolfie for a while to see if he would eat the flies.

"Wolfie looks sad," said George. "Maybe we need a bigger place to keep him."

"Let's ask my mother if she has anything bigger," Harry said.

Polly was at the kitchen table. She had a rubber band over her first finger. She pulled the rubber band back like a slingshot. A fly walked across the table. *Snap!* Polly let the rubber band go. The fly bounced over on its back.

"Wow!" said George.

Polly picked up the fly and put it into a jelly jar. There were four other flies in the jar.

"They have to be alive," said Harry. "Wolfie won't eat dead flies."

"They are alive," said Polly. "They are just stunned." She shook the jar. The flies buzzed.

Harry gave George a dirty look. "What did I tell you," he said. Harry asked his mother, "Do you have anything bigger than a jar for Wolfie?"

"Who is Wolfie?" his mother asked.

"He is a big hairy spider," said Harry.

"Harry won't let me see him," Polly said, "until I catch a hundred flies."

"A spider!" said Harry's mother. "Where is it?"

"In Biffy's house," said Polly.

Harry's mother said, "Why don't you take it to Miss Rose at the Nature Center? Biffy and Inky are enough pets for one family."

"Anybody can have a dog and a cat," Harry said.

Polly snapped her rubber band and stunned another fly. "Can I go to the Nature Center, too?" Polly asked.

"No!" said Harry. He and George ran outdoors.

The Nature Center had rocks, butterflies, other insects, and leaves. When they got there, George said, "Miss Rose, do you have something we can keep Wolfie in?"

"Who is Wolfie?" asked Miss Rose.

"Wolfgang," Harry said. "He is a wolf spider."

"Really?" Miss Rose asked. "How do you know?"

"We looked him up in a book," George said.

"He's big and brown and hairy," said Harry. "And he runs very fast. We saw him chase a bug, and he caught it, too."

"What are you feeding him?" Miss Rose asked.

"Flies," George said. "But they are very hard to catch."

"What about water?" asked Miss Rose.

"Water?" asked Harry. "Do spiders drink water?"

"Yes, they need water as much as they need food," said Miss Rose.

"I don't think he's very hungry," George said. "He hasn't made a web to catch flies."

"He won't spin a web if he is a wolf spider," said Miss Rose. "Some spiders spin webs to trap insects, but wolf spiders run after them. They are hunters. Wolf spiders do not trap insects in a web."

"Then what should we keep him in?" asked Harry.

"The best thing would be a big box with a wire screen over the top," Miss Rose said. She showed them what to do.

Miss Rose picked up a small screen. "Here," she said. "You can use this. When you have Wolfie all fixed up, will you bring him here? I'd like to see him."

"Okay," Harry said. "Thank you."

When Harry and George got home, they found an old wooden box. They put some dirt in it. They added twigs and leaves and a little clump of grass. While Harry held the screen, George dumped Wolfie into his new home. Wolfie ran into a corner and hid under a leaf.

"Let's get him some food," said Harry.

"And water," said George.

"How do you give spiders water?" asked Harry.

"I know," said a voice. It was Polly. She was sitting on the grass with Biffy and Inky.

"Go away!" said Harry.

"How *do* you give water to a spider?" asked George.

"You put drops of water on a leaf," Polly said. "Sometimes Inky drinks dewdrops that way."

"Okay, go get water," Harry said.

"Bring some flies, too," George said.

Polly brought back a jar of flies and a glass of water. "I got seven flies," she said. "Can I watch you feed Wolfie?"

"No," said Harry. "You have to get a whole hundred."

George and Harry put the flies into Wolfie's box. They sprinkled water on the leaves. Wolfie turned around. One of his legs touched a wet leaf. He seemed to be breathing heavily. He bent his knees. Then he touched the wet leaf.

"He's drinking the water!" George said. Wolfie made a dash at a fly.

"He got him!" Harry shouted. "Boy, is he fast!"

The next day Harry and George took Wolfie to Miss Rose.

"You were right," Miss Rose said. "It is a wolf spider. Did you notice how many eyes he has?"

"Eyes?" said George. "Don't insects have two eyes?"

"A spider is not an insect," Miss Rose said.

"What is it then?" Harry asked.

"An *arachnid* (uh·RAK·nid)," said Miss Rose. "Most wolf spiders have eight eyes. Bring him over to my worktable, and I will show you."

George and Harry took Wolfie's box to the table. Miss Rose got a magnifying glass and held it over the spider. He looked enormous, very hairy, and quite cross. Harry counted. Wolfie had eight eyes.

Miss Rose reached into a glass tank and picked up a shiny black beetle. It waved its legs. Miss Rose took the magnifying glass and held it over the beetle so Harry and George could see it.

"How many legs does the beetle have?" she asked.

Harry and George counted. "Six!" they said together.

"How many does Wolfie have?" Miss Rose asked.

"Those two things near his head—are they his legs?" asked George.

"No, those are palps," said Miss Rose. "Wolfie sometimes uses them to hold his food."

"Well then, he has eight legs," Harry said.

"Right," said Miss Rose. "Spiders have eight legs. Insects have six."

"Is that what makes spiders and insects different?" asked George. "Just the number of legs?"

"No," said Miss Rose. "There are other differences. Take a good look at Wolfie. How many parts does his body have?"

"He's got a head," said Harry.

"And a body," George added.

"Now look at the beetle," said Miss Rose. "How many parts does it have?" The beetle wriggled in her fingers.

"He has a head, but his body has two parts," said George.

"So he has three parts altogether," said Harry.

"He has feelers on his head, too," said George. "Wolfie doesn't have feelers."

"That's right," Miss Rose said.

"Those don't seem like very big differences," said Harry. "How else are they different?"

Miss Rose put the beetle down gently in its glass box. "Look again," she said. She put the wire screen back over the top.

"Why did we put screens over Wolfie's box and my beetle's tank?" asked Miss Rose.

"So they can have air but can't get out," Harry said.

"How would they get out?" asked Miss Rose.

"Why, Wolfie would climb right out," Harry said.

"The beetle would, too," George said. "Or he could fly out—"

"That's it!" cried Harry. "Wolfie can't fly! He doesn't have wings."

"Right you are, Harry," said Miss Rose. "Spiders don't have wings, but many insects do."

Harry and George took Wolfie back to the doghouse. Every day they watched him and fed him the flies that Polly caught. One day she caught seven, and another day she caught five. But she did not catch anywhere near a hundred.

So Polly asked Harry again, "Can't I see Wolfie now? I have twenty-seven flies."

"No," said Harry. "One hundred."

"Why?" Polly asked. "You showed him to Miss Rose. She didn't catch any flies for him."

"Of course not!" Harry said. "Miss Rose knows all about spiders! Besides, she's not a pest like you!"

"I am *not* a pest," cried Polly.

"Yes, you are," Harry said. "Go away, pest."

Polly did not catch any more flies for Wolfie that day.

When Polly went to bed, she was still mad at Harry. Inky jumped on her bed. "Harry is mean," she told Inky. "Who wants to see his old spider anyway?" she said.

In the middle of the night Polly woke up. She thought about Wolfie and the flies she had to catch before Harry would let her see him. Inky woke up and meowed softly. Polly slipped out of bed and got her flashlight. Inky followed her. They tiptoed out of the room, down the stairs, and out the back door. Silently, they crossed the yard to the doghouse.

Polly shined her flashlight inside. She crawled in and held the light over Wolfie's box. "Hello, Wolfie," she whispered.

Harry woke up, too. The moon made shadows in his room. The shadows looked like big animals with long wavy legs. Harry remembered he had not given Wolfie any water. He got out of bed and found his flashlight. He got a glass of water and crept down the stairs. The back door squeaked. Harry hoped his parents would not wake up.

Polly heard Harry coming. She turned off her flashlight and held Inky close to her.

Everything looked very different to Harry in the moonlight. The house seemed large, and the trees looked like giants. The doghouse was very dark and silent.

Harry got down on his knees to crawl inside. He pointed his flashlight at the entrance. Two yellow eyes stared at him. Harry remembered how Wolfie had looked under the magnifying glass. He almost stopped breathing. Then Harry heard a noise. It sounded like a giggle. "Wolfie?" he said.

Polly laughed.

"Polly!" cried Harry. "You rat!"

"Did I scare you?" asked Polly.

"No!" said Harry.

"Well," said Polly, "it's very dark out here. Let's go back to the house."

The next morning Polly asked Harry,
"Can I see Wolfie today?"

"You have already seen him!" said
Harry. "I guess you can."

After breakfast they took the jar of
Polly's flies to the doghouse.

"You go first," said Harry.

Polly crawled into the doghouse. "Hello,
Wolfie," said Polly.

Harry crawled in after her. Wolfie was
in his box, among the leaves.

"He's great, Harry," said Polly.

"Yes," said Harry, "he sure is." He
handed Polly the jar of flies. "Here," he
said, "you can feed Wolfie today."

Think about the story. Copy the chart on page 59. Fill in the information. Then answer the questions.

1. Use your chart. Also, think about what you know about spiders. Do you think Harry and George give Wolfie good care? Tell why you think as you do.

2. Use your chart. What does Polly do for Wolfie?

3. Why do the children have to get Wolfie's food for him?

4. Why do you think Miss Rose does not tell Harry and George to leave Wolfie in the Nature Center?

5. The boys name Wolfie for the kind of spider he is. What would you name a spider and why?

6. In what way is Wolfie one of a kind?

Discuss whether or not spiders make good pets. Ask questions about what your classmates say. Talk about the answers.

WORK IN A GROUP

You have read these selections.

The Beach
"Let's Marry!" Said the Cherry
Just the Thing for Geraldine
Spiders Are Special
Wolfie

Talk about the selections. Talk about how the ideas and characters are alike and different. Talk about the theme.

1. How is what happens to Mole and Troll like what happens to the cherry and the pea? How is what happens to each pair different?

2. How is Geraldine's special talent like a spider's special talent? How is it different?

3. Do you think Wolfie might be good at juggling? Tell why.

4. Which selection do you think is about the most unusual one-of-a-kind thing? Why do you think as you do?

BOOKSHELF

Making the Team by Nancy Carlson. Carolrhoda Books, 1985. Louanne, a pig, and her friend Arnie, a cat, find out what their talents are.

Miss Nelson Is Missing by Harry Allard and James Marshall. Houghton Mifflin, 1977. The children in Miss Nelson's class misbehave, and their teacher does not know what to do. Then one day a substitute teacher comes, and the children wish they had Miss Nelson back.

Wharton and Morton by Russell E. Erickson. Lothrop, Lee & Shepard, 1976. Warton, a toad, and his brother Morton go camping, but they are separated during a flood.

Oh, What Nonsense! collected by William Cole. Methuen, 1966. Here are fifty silly poems to make you smile and giggle.

Impossible Possum by Ellen Conford. Little, Brown, 1971. Randolph has great trouble in learning to hang by his tail. The fun begins when his sister Geraldine tricks him into hanging upside down.

2 Helping Hands

Look at the picture on pages 82 and 83. Read the title.

1. What does the title mean?

2. Who is helping in the picture? How?

3. What is the donkey doing to help?

4. What might happen if each animal does not help by playing or directing well?

5. You will read some selections. How do you think the selections will be alike?

Other Books About Helping Hands

Greff: The Story of a Guide Dog by Patricia Curtis. Lodestar Books, 1982. A Labrador retriever is shown during each stage of his training as a guide dog.

The Secret Soldier: The Story of Deborah Sampson by Ann McGovern. Four Winds Press, 1975. Deborah, disguised as a boy, is a soldier and a helping hand in the Continental Army.

Focusing on "Amelia's Roller Coaster"

▶ Describe something that was hard for you to do. Find out what kinds of things are hard for your classmates. Ask why.

▶ Look at page 86 and read the title of the story. Now read the introduction on page 87. Think about what might happen.
- What difficult thing is Amelia going to try?
- What problems might Amelia have?

▶ Get ready to read about Amelia's invention. As you read, think about how Amelia feels about her roller coaster. Think about what other people say about her invention. Also, think how to complete this chart.

Name of Person	What Each Person Feels or Says About the Roller Coaster

Now turn the page and read "Amelia's Roller Coaster." Then you will talk about daring to try.

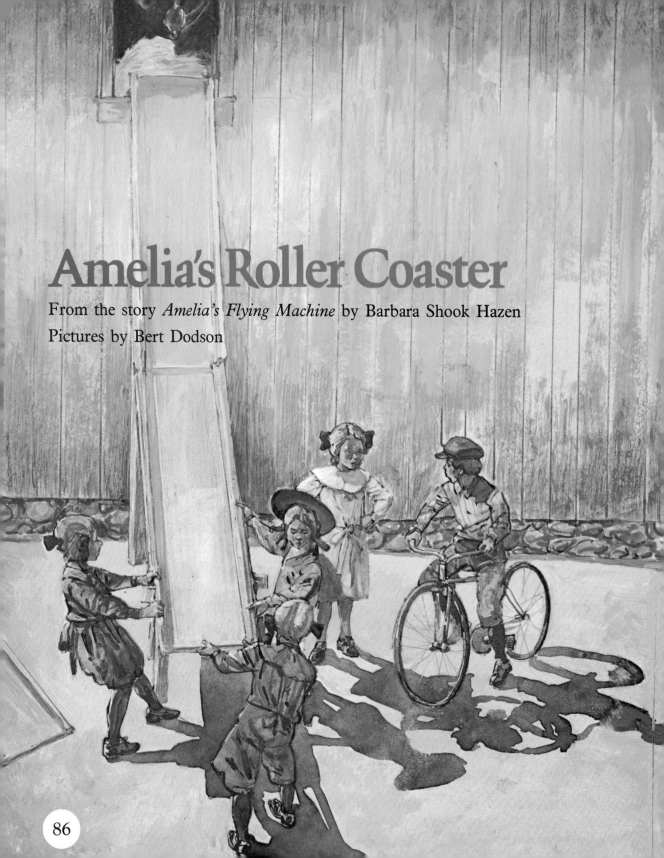

Amelia's Roller Coaster

From the story *Amelia's Flying Machine* by Barbara Shook Hazen
Pictures by Bert Dodson

A wonderful promise had been made to Amelia. Her father had promised to take her to the Chicago Fair for a roller coaster ride. She had to behave herself, though, and follow Grandma Otis's rules while her parents were away. Amelia was so excited about the roller coaster ride that she got her cousins, Katherine and Lucy, and her sister, Muriel, to help her build their own roller coaster. They constructed a wooden track leading from the barn window to the ground. They planned to come down the track in an orange crate fitted with roller skate wheels.

Trial Run

The next day, the roller coaster was ready to try out. Jimmy Watson, who lived on the neighboring farm, came over on his bike. He rode by the barn just as the girls were setting up the roller coaster.

"Not bad," said Jimmy when he saw it. "Not bad at all. But does it work? That's what I want to see."

"You will," said Amelia. "Just wait."

Jimmy leaned his bike against a tree. He sat down on the grass and watched. "Who's going to go first?" he asked.

"We could draw straws," said Amelia. "That would be fairest."

"No thanks," said Katherine. "Not me. You go first, Amelia."

"Yes, you first," said Lucy. "It was all your idea."

Muriel looked up at the track slanting out of the hayloft window and shuddered. "Not me, Meeley," she said. "It looks awfully high."

"See," Jimmy taunted. "Your sister is scared. Your cousins are scared. You're all scared to try it."

"Is that so?" said Amelia. "Well, I'm not scared. I'll gladly go first!"

Amelia tested the track to make sure it was firmly set on the ground. Then she picked up the roller coaster car. She carried it up the ladder to the hayloft and placed it on the wooden track. And then she squeezed herself inside the car. It was a tight fit.

She pushed herself part way out the barn window. She held on tight to the track sides and looked out. It was a long way down.

"What are you waiting for?" Jimmy called. "Are you scared?"

"Nope, not a bit!" said Amelia, letting go of the track sides.

The orange-crate car started to roll. It went faster and faster down the track. Amelia hugged her knees and held on tight. "Whee!" she cried. "I'm flying!"

The car gathered speed as it raced down the track. It hit the ground with a hard bump. It landed so hard that it flipped over.

Amelia flew out and fell on the ground. She lay on her stomach moaning, "Oooooooooooh!"

Katherine and Lucy and Muriel raced to her.

"Are you hurt?" asked Lucy, trying to see Amelia's face.

Even Jimmy looked worried. He held out a hand to help Amelia up. "Are you okay?" he asked.

"Sure. I'm okay," Amelia gasped. She turned herself over and brushed the dirt off her clothes.

Then she sat up and folded her arms. "I'm okay, all right," she said. "But the track isn't. The track is too short. That makes the slant too steep. And that's why the car hit the ground so hard.

"What we have to do," she said, getting up, "is add more boards and make the track longer."

"Why don't you just call it quits, huh?" suggested Jimmy.

"Not now!" said Amelia. "Not when I know what went wrong." She looked at Jimmy. "Come back this afternoon. You'll see how well it works."

Back to Work

Soon they were at it again. Amelia and Muriel laid the track on the ground. They added more boards until it was twice as long as before.

It was hard work, and it seemed even hotter than the day before. Katherine and Lucy went to the kitchen to make some lemonade.

Amelia ripped her stockings and Muriel got a splinter in her little finger. "Just a little longer," Amelia kept saying. "Just a few more boards."

They were almost done when Katherine and Lucy came back. "I hope Grandma Otis doesn't spoil everything," said Lucy. "She sounded suspicious. She wanted to know what we were up to."

"What did you tell her?" asked Amelia.

"The truth, of course," smiled Lucy. "I told her we were making lemonade and were going to take it out to you. Then I asked her if she wanted some. Then Grandma looked down her glasses and said, 'Young lady, I smell something fishy.' And I said, 'But, Grandma Otis, we haven't been near the river.'"

"And then we got out of there fast," said Katherine. She shook her head, "If Grandma decides to come out here, you're a goner."

"At least my trip to Chicago is," said Amelia.

A Second Try

When the lemonade was gone, the girls all helped to set up the track.

"It looks okay," said Amelia. "Let's just hope it works this time."

Soon Jimmy came back. "I wouldn't miss this for anything," he said with a grin.

Amelia made a face at him. Then she turned to the others. Once more she asked, "Shall we draw straws to see who goes first?"

"Not me," said Katherine. "Not after last time."

"Don't look at me," said Lucy.

Muriel shook her head. "Not me, Meeley," she said. "But if you go, I'll keep my fingers crossed."

"I knew it," said Jimmy. "You're too scared!"

Amelia stamped her foot. "That's not so," she said. "I'm not scared. Just you watch."

She climbed up to the hayloft and squeezed into the car. There she paused and took a deep breath. "It's got to work," she whispered to herself. "It's just got to."

"What are you waiting for?" teased Jimmy. "Santa Claus? Or me to try it for you?"

"Don't listen to him," yelled Lucy.

"Don't do it," said Katherine under her breath.

Muriel turned her head. She crossed as many fingers as she could. She closed her eyes tight. She didn't want to watch.

But she did want to see what was going on. When she opened her eyes to peek, she looked up and screamed, "Stop, Meeley! You can't go!"

The warning came too late. Amelia had just let go. The car started to roll. As it picked up speed, it went faster and faster down the long track.

Amelia felt the speed and the slap of wind in her face. "Wow! Look at me," she shouted. "I'm really flying!"

The orange crate kept going. It rolled to the end of the track, and then onto the ground. Amelia waved and grinned at Jimmy as she went by, and he grinned back at her.

The car finally came to a stop—right by
a pair of black-stockinged feet.

"Oh-oh," gulped Amelia, looking up.

Grandmother Otis stared down at
Amelia. Her hands were on her hips. Her
eyebrows met in a disapproving *V*.

She spoke in her slow we'll-get-to-the-bottom-of-this voice. "Amelia Mary, what are you up to? And what kind of fool contraption is this? I suspected something. And I suspect your father will have something to say when he hears about it."

Grandmother Otis tapped her foot. "Young lady, was all this your idea?" she asked. "Or did somebody put you up to it?"

Amelia groaned. Telling the truth meant missing Chicago and the Fair and going with her father and everything.

"Yes, Gram," she said in a small voice. "It was all my idea." Then she sighed deeply.

Grandma Otis sighed, too. "Amelia Mary, I daresay I don't know whatever will become of you if you . . . "

"Ma'am," Jimmy interrupted, "it really wasn't Amelia's fault. I mean, she made it and rode on it. But I guess I kind of put her up to it."

Grandmother Otis turned toward Jimmy. She squinted through her glasses. "I might have thought so," she said. "I didn't think any granddaughter of mine could do such a foolhardy thing."

She shook her finger at Jimmy. "Yes, I should have known you were behind this, Jimmy Watson. You have a habit of getting into mischief. Why, I have half a mind . . ."

Amelia jumped to her feet. "No, Grandma! Jimmy's not to blame. I'm the one who . . ."

"I don't want to listen," said Grandma Otis sternly. She picked up her skirts. "Amelia. Muriel. Girls. Come with me," she ordered.

"As for you, young man"—she squinted hard at Jimmy—"you stay right here and take down this contraption. Right now. Break it up, every bit of it, mind you."

She turned on her heels and headed for the house.

Amelia hung back. "It isn't fair," she said to Jimmy. "You're getting the blame. It was my idea."

"So what!" Jimmy shrugged. "She'll get over it, and you'll get to go to Chicago. She never tells my pa, and she won't tell yours either."

"Know something?" Amelia smiled. "You're okay."

Jimmy grinned back. "Just send me a postcard with a picture of the roller coaster on it."

The Real Amelia

Amelia's full name was Amelia Earhart
(EHR•hahrt). She grew up in the early 1900s, a
time when the first airplanes were being flown.
Not only did Amelia learn to fly, but she became
one of the finest pilots of her time.

Amelia Earhart was the first woman to fly across
the Atlantic Ocean alone. She received many honors
for her solo flight, but she wanted to do something
that no pilot had ever done. She wanted to fly
around the world at the equator—a more difficult
and dangerous route than any that had ever been
flown.

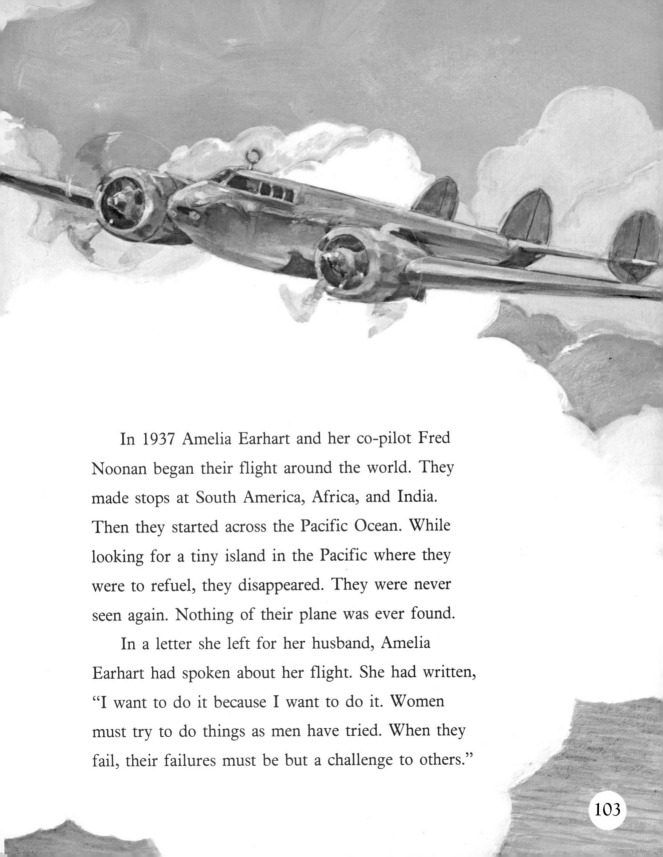

In 1937 Amelia Earhart and her co-pilot Fred Noonan began their flight around the world. They made stops at South America, Africa, and India. Then they started across the Pacific Ocean. While looking for a tiny island in the Pacific where they were to refuel, they disappeared. They were never seen again. Nothing of their plane was ever found.

In a letter she left for her husband, Amelia Earhart had spoken about her flight. She had written, "I want to do it because I want to do it. Women must try to do things as men have tried. When they fail, their failures must be but a challenge to others."

Think about the story. Copy the chart on page 85. Fill in the information. Then answer the questions.

1. Use your chart. Does Amelia or Jimmy have more faith in the roller coaster? Explain your answer.

2. How do Amelia's cousins feel about her roller coaster?

3. What problems does Amelia have at first with her invention?

4. Amelia tries a second time. What does this show about her?

5. Is Amelia's invention a success? Why or why not?

6. Why does this story belong in a unit about helping hands?

WORK IN A GROUP

List some things to invent. Think of unusual or daring things. Everyone in the group must make a suggestion. Then pick one thing that you would like to invent. Tell why you would like to make it. Make a sketch of the invention.

Focusing on "Along Sandy Trails"

▶ Talk about times you have spent outdoors with an older family member. Tell what you learned. Ask your classmates questions.

▶ Look at the picture on page 107. Now read page 106. Think about what you know about spending time outdoors with a family member.
  • What kinds of things might the girl and her grandmother talk about?
  • What might the girl learn from her grandmother?

▶ Get ready to read about a walk in the desert. Imagine that you are the girl in the story. Think about how you would complete this drawing.

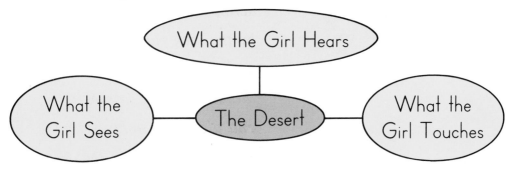

Now turn the page and read "Along Sandy Trails." Then you will talk about nature.

From

Along Sandy Trails

A story by Ann Nolan Clark
Photographs by Alfred A. Cohn

My grandmother tells me,
   "Small Papago Indian,
   girl of the Desert People,
   for two summer moons
   I will walk with you
   across the sand patches,
   by the rock ridges
   and the cacti,
   through the dry washes
   and along the sandy trails
   that you may know the desert
   and hold its beauty
   in your heart forever."

I walk with my grandmother
    along a sandy trail.
The sand beneath my feet
    is damp and cool
    because, last night
    while I was sleeping,
    clouds rained down
    upon our thirsty land.

Rain washed the flowers
    of all the cacti,
    the pincushion
    and the cholla
    (CHOH·yah),
    the hedgehog
    and the prickly pear.

We sit by the trail to rest.
Beside me a lizard's track
    is penciled lightly
    on the sand.
I touch it with my fingers.
I see a gila (HEE·lah) woodpecker
    pecking the trunk
    of a giant cactus.
If I listen . . . listen . . . listen,
    I will hear him pecking.

Along the trail
    a roadrunner runs
    all stretched out
    as if he cannot get
    to where he is going
    fast enough, soon enough.
I look and see. I listen and hear.
There are so many things
    in this quiet land.

But I like best the quail.
I watch them walking,
    their black plumes bobbing
    from their red bonnets.
They walk across the trail
    near my grandmother and me,
    so busy talking together
    they do not see us.

Quail do not hop
    as some birds do.
They walk elegantly
    with quick, small steps.
Other birds walk alone,
    but quail go everywhere
    with their families
    and their friends.
They go in coveys.

My grandmother whispers,
"Watch. Be still.
See the guard quail
sitting on the cholla,
not eating,
not talking,
just sitting.
Listen. If he calls
cra-er, cra-er, cra-er,
he is warning his covey
of danger."

Then my grandmother says,
"Down the trail a little distance
I will show you something
to remember always."
We walk along and come
to a spreading creosote.

Under its branches, on the ground,
in a round place
lined with desert grass,
is a quail's nest.
In the nest are many eggs.
One is broken.
I count them
but do not touch them
or make a noise of any kind.

112

I like best the quail.
But my grandmother likes
    the giant cactus,
    standing tall and stark
    against the sky.
Giant cactus gives us
    many important things.
The rain water stored
    in its pleated trunk
    stays our thirst
    when the winds
    of the dry moon
    sweep across our land.
Its white and yellow flower-crowns
    ripen slowly to scarlet fruit
    that we gather
    and store as food
    for the time
    of the hunger moon.

Our baskets are filled
    with the ripe fruit
    of the giant cactus
    that we have gathered,
    my grandmother and I,
    and that now we take
    to my mother's house.
The sand beneath our feet
    is deep and shifting.
The way seems long
    and our baskets are heavy.
We walk and rest.
We walk and rest.
After a time of just resting,
    happy and quiet,
    Grandmother says, "Come,
    little granddaughter.
    The sun travels westward
    to make the day's ending.
    Your father has worked
    his fields.
    Your mother has woven
    her baskets.
    Nighttime is waiting."

Think about the story. Finish the drawing on page 105. Fill in the information. Then answer the questions.

1. Use your drawing. What wild creatures does the girl see? How does she seem to feel about them?

2. What does the girl learn about how quail protect themselves? Look at the picture of the quail on page 110. What else protects the quail?

3. Why do you think the girl does not touch the quail's eggs?

4. Imagine that you are going into this desert. You do not take food and water with you. What three things would you take? Why?

5. Think about the helping hands in this story. Name two ways in which someone is helped.

6. The grandmother is teaching the girl a skill. The skill will help the girl learn on her own. What is this skill?

**WORK IN
A GROUP**

Talk with your group about the most interesting place outdoors you have been. Ask questions to learn what is special about the places your classmates like. Discuss their answers.

116

Focusing on "Mississippi Possum"

▶ Tell about some things that people your age and younger children might fear. Ask your classmates questions about their ideas.

▶ Read the story title on page 118. Now look at the pictures on pages 118–130. Think about what you know about being afraid.

- How do you think the possum feels? Why do you think that?
- What things might frighten the possum?
- What will the possum do in the story?

▶ Get ready to read about a possum. One of his fears causes him a problem. As you read, think about how to complete this chart.

Main Character _____

Setting _____

Problem _____

Solution _____

Now turn the page and read "Mississippi Possum." Then you will talk about fears.

Mississippi Possum

A story by Miska Miles
Pictures by Larry Frederick

Near the Mississippi River, a little gray possum lived in a hollow log.

When he was afraid, which was much of the time, he crept into the log and waited there.

He was afraid of many things. He was afraid of hawks and owls, of bobcats and foxes. And he was afraid of people.

When people came near, he ran into the log and was as still as he knew how to be.

There were things he was not afraid of. He was not afraid of mice or snakes, birds' eggs or berries. These, he ate.

Now, for a long time the rain had fallen and the river water rose and spread out farther along the banks. The possum looked around for food, for he had found nothing to eat for a day.

He looked up into a tree that grew beside the river, and he knew there was a bird's nest high in the branches.

He climbed up above the nest, and held a branch with his back foot, and swung by his tail to look into the nest. The nest was empty.

He climbed down again, and he looked around for berries. While he was looking he felt the earth tremble with footsteps, and he knew that something was coming down the hill, and he was afraid. He ran into his hollow log and was as still as a wild animal can be.

Jefferson Jackson and his sister Rose Mary came down the hill to look at the river.

"Look at that old Mississippi," Jefferson said. "It's getting higher and higher."

For a minute they watched. "It's coming this way," Rose Mary said. She pointed to a little stick lying on the ground. "Watch. The water's touching it." They waited.

"And now the stick's floating off," Jefferson said. "River's coming. Let's tell Papa."

They ran, pounding their feet hard against the ground.

When everything was quiet, the possum came out from his log. The brown river water was creeping along the ground toward him. Now a leaf held it back, then on it came, pushing its slow way—

He turned to go up the hill.

He traveled a long time and he came to a little brown house. He hurried past, for he knew that people lived there.

In this house, Jefferson and Rose Mary were talking to their mother and father.

"We could see the river coming higher while we watched," Jefferson said.

"Right up the hill," said Rose Mary.

"We know," said their mother. "We were about to look for you. We're going up to higher ground, where it's safe."

Quickly she reached for a basket and packed it with corn bread and a cherry pie and a handful of berries.

"The news came over the radio," their father said. "Everybody has to get out. The river's so high that it's breaking through the levee. If it breaks in many more places, it could flood right over this land. Hurry."

"Will we come back?" Rose Mary asked.

"We'll be back when the river goes down," her father said.

"That old river will pour a lot of water into the Gulf," Jefferson said. "Then everything will be just as it's always been."

Now, all this time the possum was trudging up the hill, and he saw many things.

He saw a rabbit and a dog traveling along together and the dog didn't chase the rabbit. He saw a fox and a wild turkey and the fox didn't kill the turkey.

And behind him he heard the river, and he knew he must run from it.

He heard something coming close behind him. Something else was running from the river.

There was no tree he could climb and the grasses were not thick enough for hiding. He lay down on the ground and he didn't move.

Rose Mary and Jefferson and their mother and father came up the hill.

"Look at the poor little old dead possum," Rose Mary said.

When everything was still, the possum slowly got to his feet and looked around. The river was crowding up the slope of the hill. A log floated past—maybe his own log. A boat went by and it was full of people. He saw a table floating on the water.

Far ahead were people on their way to the top of the hill, and some drove cows before them, and others led horses—

At the top of the hill, a soldier spoke to Mr. Jackson. "We have a tent for you," he said. "And there's plenty of hot food ready. Before long you'll be home again."

Rose Mary and Jefferson and their parents stood in line for food and for warm gray blankets. And afterward, they went into their tent and lay down on the earth to sleep.

"Wrapped in that blanket, you look like a gray log," Jefferson said.

But Rose Mary didn't hear, for she was asleep.

Night came, and the possum felt his
way through the grasses with his whiskers.
When he finally reached the top of the
dark hill, he was hungry and tired. He
looked in the first tent, and he thought he
saw four gray logs lying on the ground.

He sniffed the nearest. He smelled an
enemy.

Rose Mary sat up. "Papa," she said.
"Papa. I heard something."

Her father snapped on a flashlight. "I
don't see anything," he said.

"There's another little dead possum,"
she said.

"Maybe it's not dead," Jefferson said. "Maybe it's only pretending. They do, you know."

"He's an ugly fellow," her father said.

"I think he's nice-looking, for a possum," Rose Mary said. She sat down beside him and touched his rough fur. "He feels cold. He feels dead."

"Put something to eat in front of his nose and see what happens," Jefferson said.

"There are some berries in the basket," his mother said.

Rose Mary put the berries on the ground close to the possum's pointed nose.

The possum lay for a long time as though he were dead, and he hardly dared breathe, he was so frightened. Then he smelled something so good that he had to get up and look around.

The people didn't move and he was very hungry.

He ate the berries. They were fat and ripe and good. And when he had finished, the father reached out his hand, and the possum was afraid. He knew he had to climb high to be safe. He ran up along Rose Mary's arm, and she didn't move. He sat on her shoulder.

This was better than a tree. He was warm and comfortable. It was almost as good as a hollow log.

"He's getting tame," Rose Mary said. "When we go home, we can take him with us."

And during the days that passed while they waited to go home, planes flew overhead and looked for people and animals who needed help.

Steamboats churned the yellow water and pulled barges loaded with people and animals who had been rescued from the roofs of houses and barns.

Levees were built and made strong to hold the great river. And as the time passed, the possum grew tamer. He followed Rose Mary everywhere.

After a while, the river was caught behind the new levees, and it was time for everyone to go back home.

Jefferson and his mother and father and sister started down the hill, and the possum sat on Rose Mary's shoulder all the way to the little brown house near the bottom of the hill.

Then they were home, and there was a mark high on the wall to show that the Mississippi River had risen almost to the ceiling.

The possum found a hollow log near the back door to live in. Sometimes he came out and sat on Rose Mary's shoulder. More often he hunted for mushrooms or mice, and he wasn't afraid—much of the time.

Think about the story. Copy the chart on page 117. Fill in the information. Then answer the questions.

1. Look at your chart. What is the possum's problem? Why is it a problem?

2. Why does the possum pretend to be dead when Rose Mary finds him?

3. Check your chart again. What does the possum discover that helps him overcome his fear?

4. The possum climbs on Rose Mary's shoulder. Why does this make him less afraid?

5. Who do you think the helping hand in this story is? Tell why you think so.

6. Suppose there were no flood. How would this story be different?

7. Suppose the problem in this story was that Rose Mary was afraid of possums. Do you think she would have lost her fear? Why or why not?

Tell about ways to overcome fears. Ask your classmates questions about how they lost their fears. Talk about the answers.

Focusing on "The Story of a River"

▶ What does the word *river* make you think of? Quickly write everything that comes into your mind when you hear *river*. Share your thoughts with your classmates.

▶ Read the title on page 134. Now look through the pictures that go with the information story.

  • What will the information story be about?
  • What kinds of facts might you learn?

▶ Get ready to read about a river. As you read, think how people have used the river. Copy this chart and make notes on it as you read.

The River	
Group of People	Use of River

Now turn the page and read "The Story of a River." Then you will talk about how people have used the river.

The Story of a River

This is the story of a river and its people. The river could be any river, for all rivers have almost the same story. The story begins like this.

Long, long ago in the land that became America, the river began. There were no people in the land then. The young river rushed through the land. It cut through mountains. It carved deep, V-shaped valleys. It shaped the land for the people who would live there someday.

As time passed, the river cut wider valleys. The river spread out and flowed more slowly. The water was deep enough for the big boats that would someday travel on the river.

American Indians were the first people to use the river. To the Indians, the river meant life. It gave them water to drink. It was a place where food could be found—fish, turtles, and wild ducks and geese. The river also gave the Indians a fast way to travel.

Indians lived along the river before Columbus came to America. Some Indians used river clay in building their homes. Others dug ditches that carried river water to their fields. They planted corn, beans, and seeds of other crops in the rich soil of the river valleys.

135

Pictures by Bob Baumgartner and Joanna Adamska Koperska

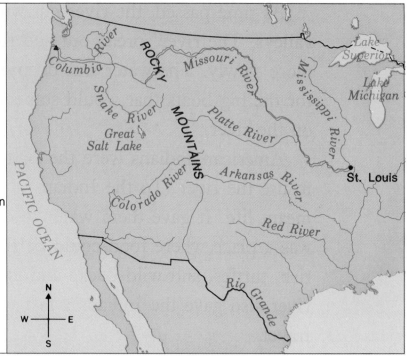

Years passed, and explorers came to America. For some explorers, the river was a highway. Its waters carried them to new lands.

Settlers followed the explorers. They came to America to make new homes. The settlers, too, came to the river. They built their homes on its banks. The river gave them water and food. Then, too, the river was beautiful. It was like a picture that was always moving and changing.

People built farms in the river's wide valleys. When the river flooded, it left rich soil on the land. The farmers did not want their farms to be flooded. Yet they knew their crops would grow well in the valleys' rich soil. So the farmers stayed in the valleys and planted their crops there, year after year.

Loggers came to the tall forests that grew on the river banks. The loggers cut down the trees and floated the logs down the river. Sawmills down the river cut the logs into boards.

More and more people came to America. The river towns grew. Where the river empties into the sea, a town became a mighty city. Today the city is a port with a deep, safe harbor. Ships from all over the world land there. They unload their goods. They take on products made in the river towns and grain grown on the farms far upriver. Then the ships carry their cargo to other places.

Many people depend on the river. They drink river water that has been treated to make it clean. They use products brought by boat up the river. They eat foods grown on the river's banks. Dams along the river produce power that lights people's homes.

The people enjoy the river, too. They admire its beauty. They enjoy swimming, fishing, and boating on the river.

Now the river is old, but its story goes on. The river is still changing. Some parts are getting deeper. In places, its path is changing. The river may one day be even slower and more shallow than it is now. Or, if the earth shifts, the river may become swifter and deeper than before. Yet no matter how the river changes, one thing will stay the same. People will use the river, and enjoy it, and become part of the story it tells.

Think about the information story. Look at the facts you wrote on your chart. Then answer these questions.

1. Use your chart. Think of the first people who settled near a river. Why did they settle there?

2. Use your chart. How and why did explorers use rivers?

3. Use your chart. Name two reasons farmers settled near rivers.

4. What happens at places where rivers run into the sea? Why does this happen?

5. What is one of the newest ways in which the river is used? Why wasn't the river used this way by the early settlers?

6. Who or what is the helping hand in this information story? Tell why you think so.

7. If you could talk to the river, what would you say?

Tell about other valuable natural resources. Ask others what they know about these resources.

WORK IN A GROUP

Focusing on "Guess Who My Favorite Person Is"

▶ Talk about some of your favorite things.
Ask others questions about what they say.

▶ Read the title on page 145. Think about what
you know about favorite things.

- Who might be saying the words of the
  title? Why do you think that?
- Will this be a story about doing things
  together or about talking together?
  Explain your answer.

▶ Get ready to read about a meeting between
two girls. They talk about favorite things. As
you read, think about what to list on this chart.

What the Girls Make Choices About	
1.	5.
2.	6.
3.	7.
4.	8.

Now turn the page and read "Guess Who
My Favorite Person Is." Then you will talk
about favorite things.

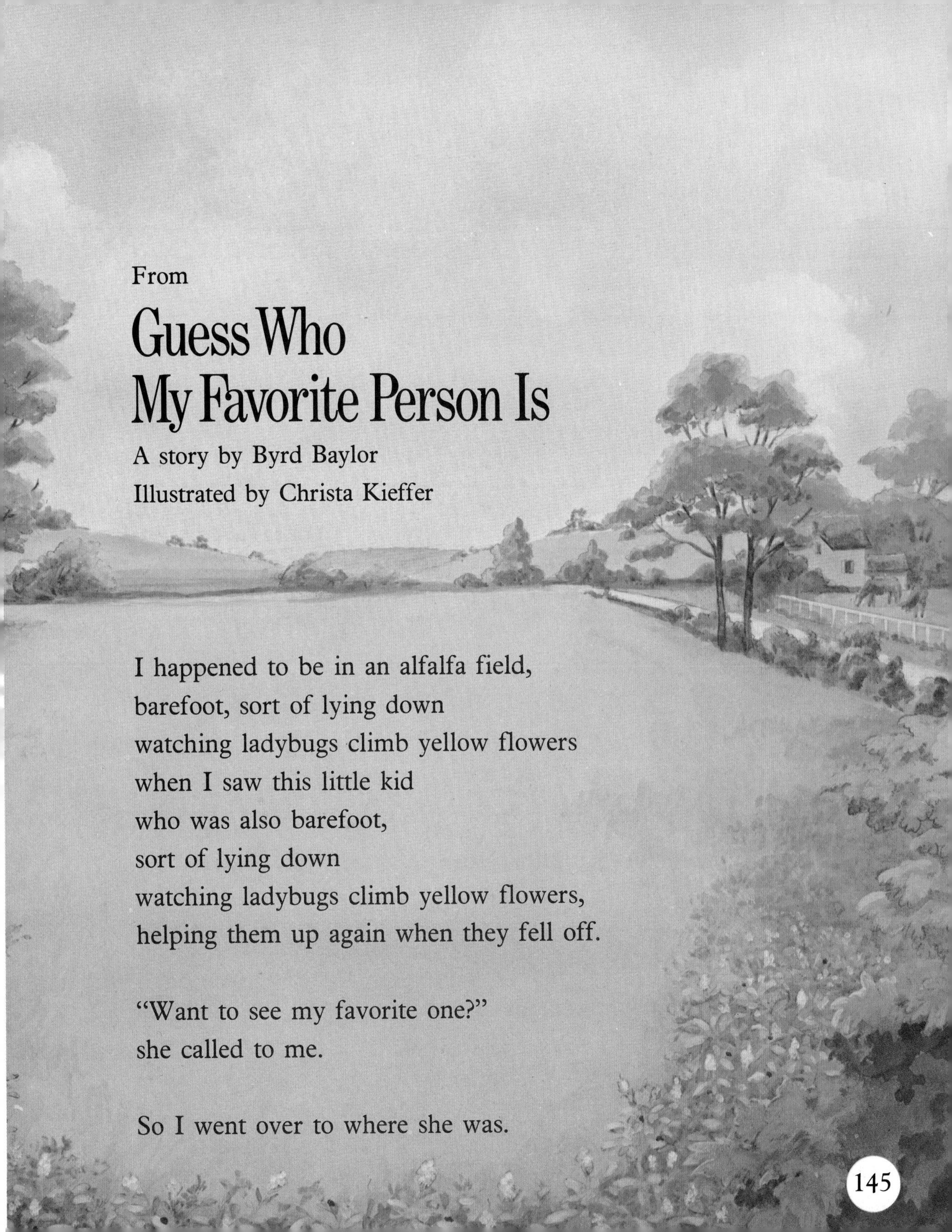

From

Guess Who My Favorite Person Is

A story by Byrd Baylor

Illustrated by Christa Kieffer

I happened to be in an alfalfa field,
barefoot, sort of lying down
watching ladybugs climb yellow flowers
when I saw this little kid
who was also barefoot,
sort of lying down
watching ladybugs climb yellow flowers,
helping them up again when they fell off.

"Want to see my favorite one?"
she called to me.

So I went over to where she was.

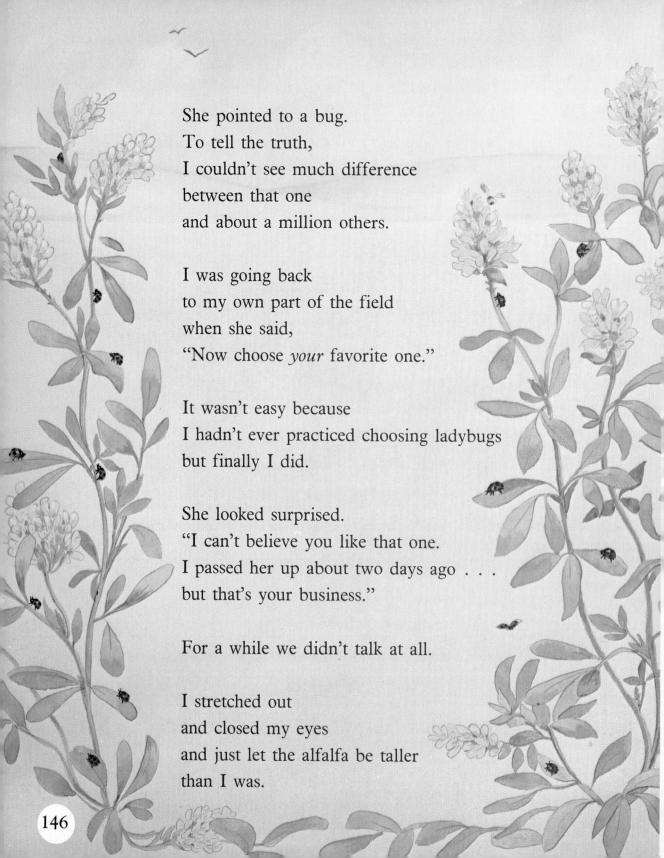

She pointed to a bug.
To tell the truth,
I couldn't see much difference
between that one
and about a million others.

I was going back
to my own part of the field
when she said,
"Now choose *your* favorite one."

It wasn't easy because
I hadn't ever practiced choosing ladybugs
but finally I did.

She looked surprised.
"I can't believe you like that one.
I passed her up about two days ago . . .
but that's your business."

For a while we didn't talk at all.

I stretched out
and closed my eyes
and just let the alfalfa be taller
than I was.

But she said,
"What's your favorite thing—
sleeping or being awake?"

"Awake," I said.

"Then wake up and we can play
the tell-what-your-favorite-thing-is game."

"I think we are already playing it,"
I said.

She said,
"We are, and it's my turn.
My favorite turn is FIRST."

So I said, "Go ahead."

She said,
"Tell me your favorite color."

I said, "Blue."

But she said,
"See, you've already done it wrong.
In this game you can't just say it's blue.
You have to say what *kind* of blue."

So I said,
"All right. You know the blue
on a lizard's belly?
That sudden kind of blue
you see just for a second sometimes—
so blue that afterwards
you always think you made it up?"

"Sure," she said.
"I know that kind of blue."

Then she told me *hers*
and it was brown.
She said, "And the brown I like the best
is a dark reddish brown
that's good for mountains and for rocks.
You see it in steep cliffs a lot."

I said,
"I know that kind of brown."

Then we chose our favorite sounds.

She said hers was *bees*
but not just one or two.
She said it takes about a thousand bees
buzzing in all the fields around
to make the kind of loud bee sound
she likes.

For mine, I chose a bird I'd heard
one morning in the mountains in New Mexico
and never saw and never heard again
and couldn't even say why
I still remembered it.

She said it was all right
that I didn't know its name.

We must have named
a hundred favorite things
that afternoon.

Her favorite thing to taste
is snow and honey mixed . . .
a little more honey than snow.

Mine is bread just baked at home,
still warm.

Her favorite smell is the alfalfa
growing in this field.

Mine is *desert* rain—
not rain anywhere else.

Finally I said,
"What's your favorite time of day?"

And she said,
"Now, just about now
when I've been running in the field
and getting out of breath
and falling down
and watching ladybugs
and finding someone to play
the tell-what-your-favorite-thing-is game
and playing it and then maybe
walking back as far as the road together."

I was going to say
that sunrise is my favorite time of day

but when I thought about it
I wanted to choose *now* too.

I wasn't sure she'd let us both
choose the same thing
but she was nice about it.

She said, "We can.
That's my favorite way
to end the game."

By then it was getting late
so we walked back as far as the road
together.

Think about the story. Copy the chart on page 143. Fill in the information. Then answer the questions.

1. Look at your chart. Also, look at the pictures on pages 150 and 151. What favorite things do these pictures show you? Which two senses do they describe?

2. What is wrong about the way the older girl first plays the game? Why is the game better after she changes the way she plays?

3. The older girl is going to choose sunrise as her favorite time. Why does she change her mind?

4. Think about the title. Who do you think is the favorite person? Why?

5. Who is the helping hand in the story?

6. One of the girls asks, "What is your favorite time of day?" How would you answer?

Tell about what makes something a favorite thing. Ask questions about what your classmates say. Talk about the answers.

WORK IN A GROUP

You have read these selections.

Amelia's Roller Coaster
Along Sandy Trails
Mississippi Possum
The Story of a River
Guess Who My Favorite Person Is

Talk about the selections. Talk about how the ideas and characters are alike and different. Talk about the theme.

1. How are the grandmother in "Along Sandy Trails" and the young girl in "Guess Who My Favorite Person Is" alike?

2. What things other than people are also helping hands in this unit?

3. How are Amelia and the Mississippi Possum different?

4. Which selection best tells about helping hands? Why do you think as you do?

BOOKSHELF

Will You Please Feed Our Cat? by James Stevenson. Greenwillow, 1987. Mary Ann and Louie are not happy about caring for a dog. The story Grandpa tells them changes how they feel.

Big City Port by Betsy Maestro and Ellen DelVecchio. Four Winds Press, 1983. Colorful ships of all kinds move in and out of a big city's harbor.

Harry's Dog by Barbara Ann Porte. Greenwillow, 1984. Harry knows his father could not have a dog when he was little because of an allergy, so Harry chooses a better present for his father.

Three Days on a River in a Red Canoe by Vera B. Williams. Greenwillow, 1981. Two cousins and their mothers buy a red canoe so they can take a weekend trip along a river.

The 329th Friend by Marjorie Weinman Sharmat. Four Winds Press, 1979. Though Emery Raccoon invites 328 guests to lunch, none of them have time to listen to him.

3 Tell Me the Name

Look at the picture on pages 156 and 157. Read the title.

1. What is happening in the picture?

2. How do the title of the unit and the picture go together?

3. Why are names important?

4. What might happen if people, places, and things did not have names?

5. You will read some selections. How do you think the selections will be alike?

Other Books About Names

Anastasia Krupnik by Lois Lowry. Houghton Mifflin, 1979. Anastasia keeps lists of what she does and does not like. She does like making lists. She does not like her name.

I Read Signs and I Read Symbols by Tana Hoban. Greenwillow, 1983. Signs and symbols you may not be aware of are explained.

Focusing on "Rumpelstiltskin"

▶ Talk about whether people always keep their promises. Ask questions about what your classmates say.

▶ Look at the title and the picture on page 160. Read page 161. Think about whether people always keep their promises.
  - What do you think is happening?
  - Who are the two people in the picture? How do you know?

▶ Get ready to read a story. As you read, think about what promises are made. Think about whether the promises are kept. Think about what you would add to this chart.

Queen		Rumpelstiltskin	
What She Says	What She Does	What He Says	What He Does

Now turn the page and read "Rumpelstiltskin." Then you will talk about keeping and breaking promises.

Rumpelstiltskin

A German folk tale

Once upon a time there was a poor miller who had a very beautiful daughter. One day the miller met with the King. The miller wanted to seem important, so he told the King that his daughter could spin straw into gold.

"Now, that is a talent worth having," said the King to the miller. "If your daughter is as clever as you say, bring her to my palace tomorrow. I will put her to the test."

When the girl was brought to the palace, the King led her into a room full of straw. There he gave her a spinning wheel and spindle.

"Now set to work and spin all night," said the King. "If by dawn you have not spun the straw into gold, you shall die."

Then he locked the door behind him and left her alone inside.

The poor girl sat down and did not know what she was to do. At last she became so miserable that she began to cry.

Suddenly the door opened.
In stepped a tiny little man.

"Good evening. Why are you crying so
bitterly?" he asked.

163

"Oh!" answered the girl. "I have to spin this straw into gold, and I do not know how to do it."

"What will you give me if I spin it for you?" asked the little man.

"My necklace," replied the girl.

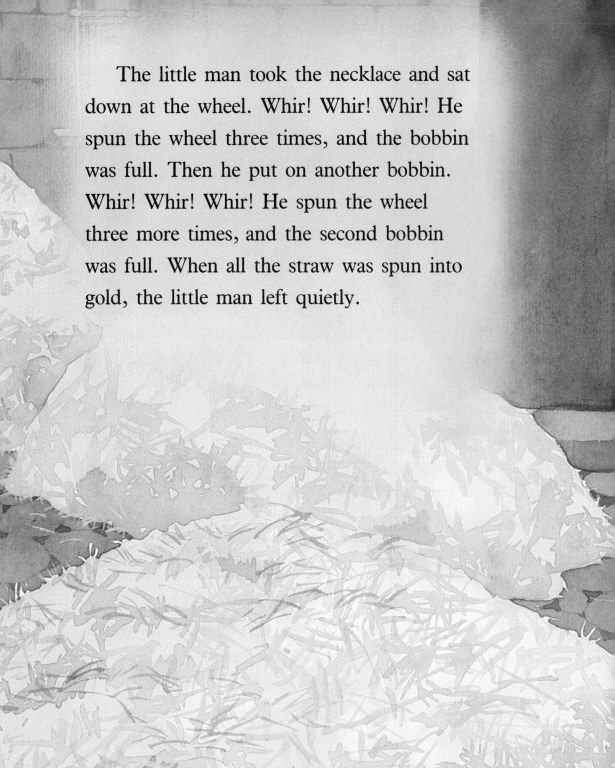

The little man took the necklace and sat
down at the wheel. Whir! Whir! Whir! He
spun the wheel three times, and the bobbin
was full. Then he put on another bobbin.
Whir! Whir! Whir! He spun the wheel
three more times, and the second bobbin
was full. When all the straw was spun into
gold, the little man left quietly.

The next morning, the King was delighted to see the gold. He led the miller's daughter to a larger room full of straw. Again he told her she must spin the straw into gold before the following morning, or she shall die.

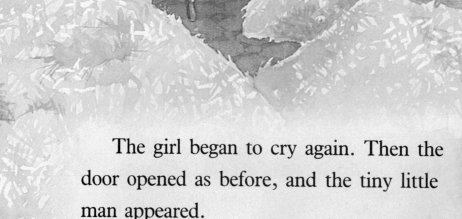

The girl began to cry again. Then the door opened as before, and the tiny little man appeared.

"What will you give me if I spin the straw into gold for you?" he asked.

"The ring from my finger," answered the girl.

The little man took the ring, and 'round went the spinning wheel again. By morning he had spun all the straw into glittering gold.

The King was very pleased, but he still wanted more gold. He had the miller's daughter taken into an even larger room full of straw.

"You must spin all of this straw into gold during the night. If you succeed this time, you shall become my wife," said the King.

When the girl was alone, the little man appeared for the third time.

"What will you give me if I spin the straw for you once again?" he asked.

"I have nothing more to give," answered the girl.

"Then promise to give me your first child when you are Queen," said the little man.

"Who knows if that will happen?" thought the miller's daughter.

So she promised the little man what he had asked. He set to work once more and spun the straw into gold.

When the King came in the morning,
he found the gold. He quickly married the
miller's daughter and made her Queen.

After a year had passed, a beautiful son was born to the Queen. She thought no more of the little man. Then all of a sudden, one day he stepped into her room.

"Now give me what you promised," demanded the little man.

The Queen was very upset.

"I will give you all the riches in my kingdom, if you allow me to keep my child," said the Queen.

"No, a young boy is dearer to me than all the treasures in the world," said the little man.

Then the Queen began to cry, and the little man felt sorry for her.

"I will give you three days to guess my name," he said. "If you find it out in that time, you may keep your child."

That night the Queen thought of all the names she had ever heard. She also sent a messenger to search the land for different names.

The little man arrived on the following day.

"Is your name Kasper?" the Queen asked.

"That is not my name."

"Is your name Melchior?" she asked next.

"That is not my name."

"Then is it Belshazzar?"

"That is not my name," he replied.

The queen guessed many more names, but not one was correct.

The next day the Queen asked for the names of all the people in the neighborhood. She wrote a long list of the most uncommon names. Then the little man arrived. The Queen began to guess names again.

"Is your name, perhaps, Sheepshanks?" she asked.

"That is not my name," gleefully answered the little man.

"Is it Cruickshanks or Spindleshanks?"

"Neither is my name!" replied the little man.

After every name the Queen supplied, the little man answered, "That is not my name."

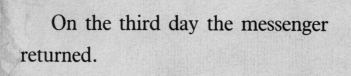

On the third day the messenger
returned.

"I have not been able to find any new
names," he said. "However, I saw a
strange sight. Far in the corner of the
wood, I saw a tiny little house. In front of
the house burned a fire. Around the fire
danced a tiny little man. He was crying:

'Tomorrow I brew, today I bake,
And then the Queen's child I will take;
For little knows my royal dame
That Rumpelstiltskin is my name!' "

You may imagine how happy the Queen was to hear the name. That same evening the little man appeared.

"Now, my lady Queen, what is my name?" he asked.

"Is your name Conrad?" she asked.

"No, that is not my name," he answered.

"Is your name Harry?"

"No."

"Is your name, perhaps, Rumpelstiltskin?"

"Who has told you that?" screamed the little man.

In his rage he stamped his right foot far into the ground. When he stamped his left foot, a large hole opened up beneath him. He disappeared into the hole and was never seen again.

Think about the story. Copy the chart on page 159. Fill in the information. Then answer the questions.

1. Use your chart. What are the first two things the Queen promises Rumpelstiltskin? What does Rumpelstiltskin do in return?

2. Use your chart. Soon the Queen has nothing left to give to Rumpelstiltskin. What does she do then and why? What does Rumpelstiltskin do and why?

3. Rumpelstiltskin asks the Queen to promise to give him her first-born baby. Is that fair? Tell why or why not.

4. The Queen has help finding Rumpelstiltskin's name. Is that fair? Tell why or why not.

5. Pretend you are the teller of this folk tale. Tell an ending that is a happy one for both the Queen and Rumpelstiltskin.

6. Suppose the Queen did not guess Rumpelstiltskin's name. Would this story belong in a unit about telling names?

Tell what keeping and breaking promises means to you. Ask questions about what your classmates say. Talk about the answers.

Focusing on "Paper Boats" and "Oliphaunt"

▶ Quickly write down how you feel the first time you go to a new place. Share your writing with your classmates. Compare how you feel. Ask questions about what they say.

▶ Look at the titles and the pictures on pages 182–184. Think about what you know about going to new places.
  • Where do you think each poem takes place? What makes you think so?
  • What might happen in these poems?

▶ Get ready to read two poems. Think about the main idea of each poem. Then think about how to complete this chart.

Main Idea	
"Paper Boats"	"Oliphaunt"

Now turn the page and read "Paper Boats" and "Oliphaunt." Then you will talk about meeting others from strange lands.

Paper Boats

A poem by Rabindranath Tagore

Day by day I float my paper boats one by one down
the running stream.

In big black letters I write my name on them and
the name of the village where I live.

I hope that someone in some strange land will
find them and know who I am.

I load my little boats with *shiuli* flowers from
our garden, and hope that these blooms of dawn
will be carried safely to land in the night.

I launch my paper boats and look up into the sky
and see the little clouds setting their white
bulging sails.

I know not what playmate of mine in the sky sends
them down the air to race with my boats!

When night comes I bury my face in my arms and
dream that my paper boats float on and on
under the midnight stars.

The fairies of sleep are sailing in them, and the
lading is their baskets full of dreams.

Picture by Christa Kieffer

183

Oliphaunt

A poem by J. R. R. Tolkien

Gray as a mouse,
Big as a house,
Nose like a snake,
I make the earth shake,
As I tramp through the grass;
Trees crack as I pass.
With horns in my mouth
I walk in the South,
Flapping big ears.
Beyond count of years
I stump round and round,
Never lie on the ground,
Not even to die.
Oliphaunt am I,
Biggest of all,
Huge, old, and tall.
If ever you'd met me,
You wouldn't forget me.
If you never do,
You won't think I'm true;
But old Oliphaunt am I,
And I never lie.

Picture by Sharon Harker

Think about the poems. Copy the chart on page 181. Fill in the information. Then answer the questions.

1. Use your chart. Why does the writer sail paper boats?

2. Does the writer care to which strange land the boats might sail? Tell why you think as you do.

3. Which poem tells more about the place where the speaker of the poem lives? Explain your answer.

4. The writer sails boats down a running stream. How might the poem be different if the writer sailed the boats on a pond?

5. Pretend you want someone in a strange land to know about you and your land. How would you send the information?

6. Why do these poems belong in a unit about telling names?

**WORK IN
A GROUP**

Tell about a strange land you would like to visit. Ask your classmates questions about their choices. Talk about the answers.

Focusing on "Rufus M."

▶ Talk about what you know about using public libraries. Ask your classmates questions.

▶ Look at the picture on page 188. Read the title on page 189. Think about what you know about public libraries.
  - What do you think is happening?
  - Who is in the picture? How do you know?
  - What might happen in this story?

▶ Get ready to read a story about a young boy who wants very much to do something. As you read, think about what he wants to do and how he tries to do it. Think about what you would add to this chart.

Rufus M.	
His Problems	His Solutions

Now turn the page and read "Rufus M." Then you will talk about wanting to do something.

From

Rufus M.

A story by Eleanor Estes
Pictures by Susan Lexa

Rufus Moffat wanted a book. His older brother and his sisters were reading library books, but they said he was too young. Besides, he couldn't even read yet. That made Rufus mad. He knew how to get to the library by himself. He even knew where to find one of the Brownie books he liked. Reading? It was easy. Flipping pages. He could do that. It would be just as easy to take a book out of the library. So Rufus went to the library, chose his book, and handed it to the lady behind the desk.

"Do you have a card?" the lady asked.

Rufus felt in his pockets. Sometimes he carried around an old playing card or two. Today he didn't have one.

"No," he said.

"You'll have to have a card to get a book."

"I'll go and get one," said Rufus.

The lady put down her cards. "I mean a library card," she explained kindly. "It looks to me as though you are too little to have a library card. Do you have one?"

"No," said Rufus. "I'd like to though."

"I'm afraid you're too little," said the lady. "You have to write your name to get one. Can you do that?"

Rufus nodded his head confidently. Writing. Lines up and down. He'd seen that done. And the letters that Mama had tied in bundles in the closet under the stairs were covered with writing. Of course he could write.

"Well, let's see your hands," said the lady.

Rufus obligingly showed this lady his
hands, but she did not like the look of them.
She cringed and clasped her head as
though the sight hurt her.

"Oh," she gasped. "You'll just have to
go home and wash them before we can even
think about joining the library and borrowing
books."

This was a complication upon which
Rufus had not reckoned. However, all it
meant was a slight delay. He'd wash his
hands and then he'd get the book. He
turned and went out of the library, found his
scooter safe among the Christmas trees, and
pushed it home. He surprised Mama by
asking to have his hands washed. When this
was done, he mounted his scooter again and
returned all the long way to the library. It
was not just a little trip to the library. It was
a long one. A long one and a hot one on a
day like this. But he didn't notice that. All he
was bent on was getting his book and taking
it home and reading with the others on the
front porch. They were all still there,
brushing flies away and reading.

Again Rufus hid his scooter in the pine trees, encircled the light, and went in.

"Hello," he said.

"Well," said the lady. "How are they now?"

Rufus had forgotten he had had to wash his hands. He thought she was referring to the other Moffats. "Fine," he said.

"Let me see them," she said, and she held up her hands.

Oh! His hands! Well, they were all right, thought Rufus, for Mama had just washed them. He showed them to the lady. There was a silence while she studied them. Then she shook her head. She still did not like them.

"Ts, ts, ts!" she said. "They'll have to be cleaner than that."

Rufus looked at his hands. Supposing he went all the way home and washed them again, she still might not like them. However, if that is what she wanted, he would have to do that before he could get the Brownie book . . . and he started for the door.

"Well now, let's see what we can do," said the lady. "I know what," she said. "It's against the rules but perhaps we can wash them in here." And she led Rufus into a little room that smelled of paste where lots of new books and old books were stacked up. In one corner was a little round sink and Rufus washed his hands again. Then they returned to the desk. The lady got a chair and put a newspaper on it. She made Rufus stand on this because he was not big enough to write at the desk otherwise.

Then the lady put a piece of paper covered with a lot of printing in front of Rufus, dipped a pen in the ink well and gave it to him.

"All right," she said. "Here's your application. Write your name here."

All the writing Rufus had ever done before had been on big pieces of brown wrapping paper with lots of room on them. Rufus had often covered those great sheets of paper with his own kind of writing at home. Lines up and down.

But on this paper there wasn't much space. It was already covered with writing. However, there was a tiny little empty space and that was where Rufus must write his name, the lady said. So, little space or not, Rufus confidently grasped the pen with his left hand and dug it into the paper. He was not accustomed to pens, having always worked with pencils until now, and he made a great many holes and blots and scratches.

"Gracious," said the lady. "Don't bear down so hard! And why don't you hold it in your right hand?" she asked, moving the pen back into his right hand.

Rufus started again scraping his lines up and down and all over the page, this time using his right hand. Wherever there was an empty space he wrote. He even wrote over some of the print for good measure. Then he waited for the lady, who had gone off to get a book for some man, to come back and look.

"Oh," she said as she settled herself in her swivel chair, "is that the way you write? Well . . . it's nice, but what does it say?"

"Says Rufus Moffat. My name."

Apparently these lines up and down did not spell Rufus Moffat to this lady. She shook her head.

"It's nice," she repeated. "Very nice. But nobody but you knows what it says. You have to learn to write your name better than that before you can join the library."

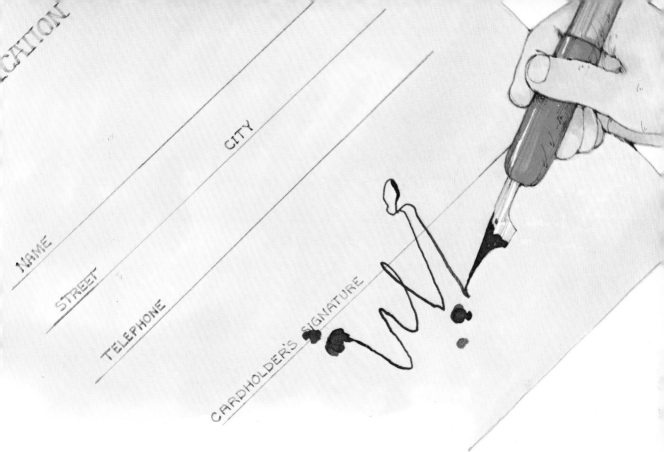

Rufus was silent. He had come to the library all by himself, gone back home to wash his hands, and come back because he wanted to take books home and read them the way the others did. He had worked hard. He did not like to think he might have to go home without a book.

The library lady looked at him a moment and then she said quickly before he could get himself all the way off the big chair, "Maybe you can *print* your name."

Rufus looked at her hopefully. He thought
he could write better than he could print, for
his writing certainly looked to him exactly
like all grown people's writing. Still he'd try
to print if that was what she wanted.

The lady printed some letters on the top
of a piece of paper. "There," she said.
"That's your name. Copy it ten times and
then we'll try it on another application."

Rufus worked hard. He worked so hard
the knuckles showed white on his brown fist.

He worked for a long, long time, now with his right hand and now with his left. Sometimes a boy or a girl came in, looked over his shoulder and watched, but he paid no attention. From time to time the lady studied his work and she said, "That's fine. That's fine." At last she said, "Well, maybe now we can try." And she gave him another application.

All Rufus could get, with his large generous letters, in that tiny little space where he was supposed to print his name, was R-U-F. The other letters he scattered here and there on the card. The lady did not like this either. She gave him still another blank. Rufus tried to print smaller and this time he got RUFUS in the space, and also he crowded an M at the end. Since he was doing so well now the lady herself printed the *offat* part of Moffat on the next line.

"This will have to do," she said. "Now take this home and ask your mother to sign it on the other side. Bring it back on Thursday and you'll get your card."

Rufus's face was shiny and streaked with dirt where he had rubbed it. He never knew there was all this work to getting a book. The other Moffats just came in and got books. Well, maybe they had had to do this once too.

Rufus held his hard-earned application in one hand and steered his scooter with the other. When he reached home Joey, Jane and Sylvie were not around any longer. Mama signed his card for him, saying, "My! So you've learned how to write!"

"Print," corrected Rufus.

Mama kissed Rufus and he went back out. The lady had said to come back on Thursday, but he wanted a book today. When the other Moffats came home, he'd be sitting on the top step of the porch, reading. That would surprise them. He smiled to himself as he made his way to the library for the third time.

When he reached home, he showed Mama his book. She smiled at him, and gave his cheek a pat. She thought it was fine that he had gone to the library and joined all by himself and taken out a book. And she thought it was fine when Rufus sat down at the kitchen table, was busy and quiet for a long, long time, and then showed her what he had done.

He had printed RUFUS M. That was what he had done. And that's the way he learned to sign his name. And that's the way he always did sign his name for a long, long time.

About
ELEANOR ESTES

Though she always wanted to become a writer, Eleanor Estes (EHS•teez) said, "I never really decided to write for children. It just happened that I did." She has filled her warm and funny stories with many memories of her own childhood. Often, in the middle of the night, she would remember what someone said or did. She wrote these memories down, and later used them in the stories she wrote.

Eleanor Estes grew up in West Haven, Connecticut. After graduating from high school, she worked as a librarian. When her first book, *The Moffats,* was published, she decided to become a full-time writer. Several of her books are about the adventures of the Moffat family.

More Books by Eleanor Estes

The Hundred Dresses
The Middle Moffat
Ginger Pye
The Moffat Museum

Think about the story. Copy the chart on page 187. Fill in the information. Then answer the questions.

1. Use your chart. What does Rufus want from the library? Why is he unable to get it?

2. Why does the librarian want Rufus to fill out an application?

3. Why does Rufus have to tell the librarian his name?

4. Why does Rufus want a library card?

5. Rufus goes to the library three times in one day to get what he wants. Do you think he returned to the library often after that day? Tell why you think as you do.

6. Pretend you are there when Rufus tries to read his book. What do you think happens?

7. Why does this story belong in a unit about telling names?

Talk about something you very much want to do. Ask questions about what your classmates say. Talk about the answers.

Focusing on
"The Naming of Olga da Polga"

▶ Talk about what you know about pets. Ask your classmates questions to learn more about what they know.

▶ Look at the pictures on pages 206–216. Think about what you know about pets.
- Who is in the pictures? What makes you think as you do?
- What might happen in this story?

▶ Get ready to read a story about a young girl and her pet guinea pig. As you read, think about how the girl chooses a name for her pet. Think about how to complete this chart.

How Olga Gets Her Name		
Event 1	Event 2	Event 3

Now turn the page and read "The Naming of Olga da Polga." Then you will talk about the importance of a name.

The Naming of
Olga da Polga

A story from *The Tales of Olga da Polga* by Michael Bond
Pictures by Mike Muir

Olga da Polga lived in a crowded pet shop with a lot of other guinea pigs. Yet Olga da Polga wasn't like the others. She had a gleam in her eyes, an unusual name, and big dreams about "going places." The other guinea pigs were afraid of the outside world, but Olga could hardly wait to get there.

One day, quite suddenly, Olga da Polga's dreams came true. A man and his daughter came into the shop, bought Olga da Polga, and took her home.

If Olga da Polga's new home wasn't exactly a palace it certainly seemed like it, and it was definitely the nearest she was ever likely to get to one.

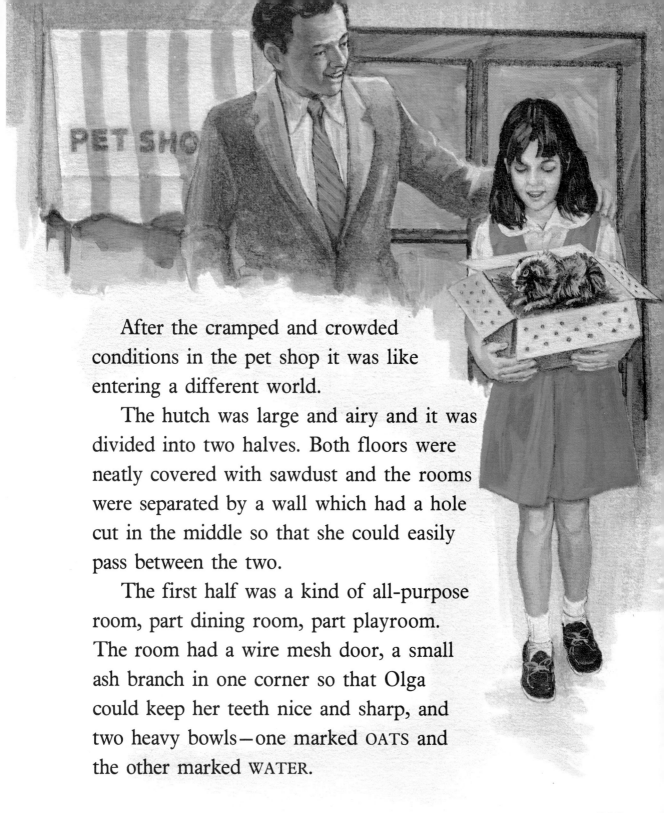

After the cramped and crowded
conditions in the pet shop it was like
entering a different world.

The hutch was large and airy and it was
divided into two halves. Both floors were
neatly covered with sawdust and the rooms
were separated by a wall which had a hole
cut in the middle so that she could easily
pass between the two.

The first half was a kind of all-purpose
room, part dining room, part playroom.
The room had a wire mesh door, a small
ash branch in one corner so that Olga
could keep her teeth nice and sharp, and
two heavy bowls—one marked OATS and
the other marked WATER.

Olga tried out both before turning her attention to the second room. This turned out to be even more exciting than the first, for it not only had a *glass window* to keep out the weather, but there was a large, inviting mound of fresh-smelling hay as well.

Olga spent some time pressing the hay flat so that she would have somewhere comfortable to sleep without being too hot, and then she settled down to think things over.

Really, all things considered, life had taken a very pleasant turn.

The sun was shining. The birds were chirping. Even the noises seemed friendly. Olga enjoyed the clinkings, singing,

and occasional humming sounds from somewhere inside the big house as Mr. and Mrs. Sawdust—which was what Olga had decided to call them—went about their work.

Every so often there was a reassuring murmur of voices outside as one or other of the family peered through the glass to make certain she was all right.

First came Mr. Sawdust, then Mrs. Sawdust, then some other people called "neighbors" and they all had a friendly word or two to say to her.

Finally Karen Sawdust herself arrived with an enormous pile of grass, a bunch of dandelions, and a large juicy carrot neatly sliced down the center, which she placed temptingly alongside the feeding bowl.

"We're going to choose a name for you now," Karen announced, as Olga stirred herself and came out of the bedroom to sample these new delicacies. "And we have to make sure it's right because tomorrow Daddy's going to paint it over your front door. There'll be no changing it once that's done."

Olga nibbled away, half listening, half in a world of her own.

"Daddy fancies Greta and Mummy's rather keen on Gerda, but I'm not sure. They don't sound *special* enough to me." Karen Sawdust put her face against the door as she turned to go. "I do wish you could tell us what *you* would like for a name."

"Greta? . . . Gerda? . . . *Painted on my front door?*" Olga's world suddenly turned upside down.

She paused, a carefully folded piece of grass half in, half out of her mouth, hardly able to believe her ears.

"But I'm Olga da Polga," she wailed, addressing the empty air. "I've always been Olga da Polga. I can't change now—I really can't." That night, long after darkness fell and everyone else had gone to bed, Olga was still wide awake and deep in thought.

"I suppose," she said to herself, for what seemed like the hundredth time, "I suppose I ought to be counting my blessings instead of grumbling. I mean . . . I have a nice new home . . . food . . . I'm among friends . . . but I *would* like to keep my own name, especially as I'm having it painted on."

The more Olga thought about it the sadder she became, for she couldn't help remembering a remark one of the older inhabitants of the pet shop had once made. "Always hang on to your name," he had said. "It may not be much, but when you're a guinea pig it's sometimes all you have in the world."

Olga's own name was firmly imprinted on her mind. OLGA DA POLGA.

It had taken her fancy straight away and now she had become so used to it she couldn't begin to picture having anything else. When she closed her eyes she could still see it written in large block letters on the side of an old cardboard box.

Suddenly she jumped up in excitement, her mind in a whirl. Could she? Was it possible?

It would mean a lot of hard work. A lot of difficult, almost impossible work. And yet . . .

Getting out of her warm bed, shivering partly with the chill of the night air and partly with she knew not what, Olga made her way through into the next room.

Clutching the ash branch firmly in her mouth she set to work. Scratching and scraping, starting and stopping, she worked and she worked and she worked. Sometimes pausing to smooth the sawdust over before beginning all over again, she tried not once, but time after time and still it wouldn't come right.

Dawn was breaking before she crawled
back into her bedroom at long last and
sank down in the hay. Her paws were
aching, her fur was covered in sawdust, and
her eyes were so tired she could hardly
bear to keep them open.

"It looks plain enough to me," she thought, gazing back at the result of her night's work, "but then, I *know* what it's meant to be. I only hope the others understand as well."

Gradually, as she enjoyed her well-earned rest, the air began to fill with sounds of morning. They were strange, unaccustomed sounds. In place of the usual grunts and rustles of the pet shop there were dogs barking, clocks striking, the sound of bottles clinking, and somewhere in the distance the noise of a train rattling on its way. In fact, there were so many different noises Olga soon lost count of them.

And then, at long last, came the one she had been waiting for. There was a click, the clatter of a bolt being withdrawn, and a moment later a now familiar face appeared on the other side of the wire netting.

In the pause which followed, Olga could almost hear the beating of her own heart.

"Mummy! Mummy!" With a shriek of surprise the face vanished from view. "Come quickly! Come and see!"

Olga jumped to her feet. "Wheeee! It's worked! It's worked! Wheeeeeee!" Squeaking with joy and pleasure at her own cleverness she ran round and round her dining room, scattering sawdust and the result of her labors in one wild whirlwind of delight.

"Olga da Polga?" exclaimed the voice of Mrs. Sawdust. "Written on the floor? Don't be silly . . . how *could* it have been?"

A face appeared at Olga's door. "I can't see anything at all. You must have been dreaming. All the same"—there was a pause—"it *is* rather a nice name. If I were you I'd keep it."

When they were alone again, Olga looked out of her window at Karen Sawdust and Karen Sawdust looked back at her.

"Grownups!" said Karen with a sigh. "They *never* understand these things. Still, we know it happened, don't we?"

Olga da Polga lifted up her head proudly. "Wheeee!" she cried, in the loudest voice she could possibly manage. "Wheeee! Wheeee! Wheeeeeeeee!"

And really, there was nothing more to be said.

Think about the story. Copy the chart on page 205. Fill in the information. Then answer the questions.

1. Why does Olga need a name?

2. Use your chart. Which two names does Karen tell Olga she might be named?

3. Use your chart. How do Karen and Olga feel about the two names? Tell why.

4. Why do you think Karen tells Olga about the name choices?

5. How does Olga feel about keeping the name Olga da Polga? How do you know?

6. Think about the story "Rufus M." How is that story like this one?

7. Olga prints her name in sawdust. How else might she have told Karen her name?

8. Why does this story belong in a unit about telling names?

WORK IN A GROUP

Talk about why a name is important. Ask questions about what your classmates say. Talk about the answers.

Focusing on
"Names and Their Meanings"

▶ Talk about what you know about how you were named. Ask your classmates questions.

▶ Look at the title and the subtitles on pages 220–226. Think about names.
  - What information does the title give you?
  - How do the subtitles help you know what this article might be about?

▶ Get ready to read an information story. As you read, think about names and their meanings. Copy this chart. Fill in facts as you read.

Names	Their Meanings
Animal Names	
Plant Names	
Place Names	

Now turn the page and read "Names and Their Meanings." Then you will talk about how some things got their names.

Connections

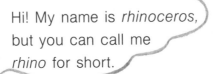

Where did you get that name?

Hi! My name is *rhinoceros*, but you can call me *rhino* for short.

Names and Their Meanings

Animal Names

How did animals get their names? Some animals were named from words that describe them. The *rhinoceros* (ry·NOS·ur·us) got its name that way. More than two thousand years ago, Greeks marched into India. There they saw a large animal that was new to them. It had a horn on its nose. The Greeks wondered what to call this great beast. They made up the name *rhinokeras* from two Greek words. The words are *rhino,* meaning "nose," and *kersos,* meaning "horn." The name *rhinoceros* came from that first name, *rhinokeras.*

The rhino's horn is not what it appears to be. Instead of being bony, the horn is made of hairs! The hairs are packed tightly together. If the horn breaks, the rhinoceros can grow a new one.

The *moose* was named by a word that tells how it eats. Algonquian (al·GONG·kwee·un) Indians saw that this animal strips tree branches bare. They named the animal *moosu*. The word means "he strips off" or "he eats off."

Study the pictures of the animals below. Read about their names. Decide why each animal was given its name.

Armadillo is a Spanish word meaning "little armored one."

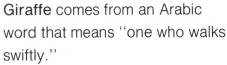

Giraffe comes from an Arabic word that means "one who walks swiftly."

Bear comes from the Old English word *bera,* meaning "brown."

Porcupine comes from two Latin words: *porcus,* "pig," and *spina,* "spine" or "thorn."

Pictures by Larry Frederick and Joanna Adamska Koperska

pitcher plant

ghost flower

cattails

Plant Names

Like animal names, names for plants often describe the plants. The leaves of the *pitcher plant* look like the spout of a pitcher. The leaves hold water, too. Rain falls into them and collects there. Insects come to eat the sweet liquid on the upper leaves. The insects slip down inside the "pitcher" and drown. They become the plant's food.

The *ghost flower* grows in dark forests. It is white and strange looking. Many people call this plant the *Indian pipe.* It looks like a little, long-stemmed Indian peace pipe.

Plants called *cattails* grow in marshy areas. These plants have fuzzy brown tips that really do look like cats' tails. The fuzz is made of tiny brown flowers.

The *sunflower* bloom looks like the sun. The bloom turns to follow the sun from sunrise to sunset, too. Long ago, the Greeks told a story about how there came to be a sunflower.

The story tells of Clytie (CLY•tee), a water maiden. One day she left the ocean. She climbed to the top of Mount Olympus (oh•LIM•pus), which was the home of the gods. There she saw the sun god, Apollo. Clytie fell in love with him, but Apollo loved another, which made Clytie sad.

Clytie sank to the ground. She turned her face to the sun. She watched the sun travel across the sky, day after day. After many days, she grew roots. She changed into a flower—a sunflower.

Tallahassee
FLORIDA

Chicago •
ILLINOIS

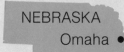

NEBRASKA
Omaha •

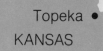

Topeka •
KANSAS

WASHINGTON
Walla Walla

Place Names

The names of places are bits of history. They often give clues about who settled in a place. In the United States, names like *New England* and *New Hampshire* tell of people who left an old home for a new one. Spanish and French names recall early explorers and settlers. City names like *Washington* and *Lincoln* honor people who are important in United States history. American Indian names remind us of the first Americans.

About half the states have American Indian names. *Kansas* means "a breeze near the ground." *Michigan* means "great water." *Texas* means "friends." *Idaho* means "good morning." The chart below gives some more American Indian place names and their meanings.

Place Name	Meaning
Tallahassee (Florida)	"old town"
Chicago (Illinois)	"wild onion place"
Omaha (Nebraska)	"those who go upstream"
Topeka (Kansas)	"good place to dig roots"
Walla Walla (Washington)	"much water"

Many places in the South and Southwest have Spanish names. Look at this map of New Mexico. Find the *Rio Grande* (REE·oh grand). This name means "great river" in Spanish. The name of the capital, *Santa Fe*, means "holy faith." *Los Alamos* (los Al·uh·mos) means "poplar trees."

NEW MEXICO

Here are some other Spanish place names. *Las Vegas* (Nevada) means "the meadows."

El Paso (Texas) was first called *El Paso del Rio.* It means "a place where the river can be crossed by wading."

French settlers also gave place names to this country. *Vermont* comes from two French words: *vert* (VAIR), meaning "green," and *mont,* meaning "mountain." *Baton Rouge* (Louisiana) was named from two French words: *baton,* meaning "stick," and *rouge,* meaning "red." Its name means "red stick." The city was named Baton Rouge because Indians put a red stick there to mark a boundary.

225

Lincoln
NEBRASKA

Madison
WISCONSIN

Carson City
NEVADA

Houston
TEXAS

The names of famous people also dot the U.S. map. Many counties, cities, and towns are named for presidents, such as *Washington, Lincoln, Jefferson, Monroe,* and *Madison. Dallas* (Texas) and *Fairbanks* (Alaska) were named after vice presidents. *Carson City,* Nevada, was named for the Western scout Kit Carson. *Houston* (HYOOS•tun), Texas, was named for General Sam Houston, who fought for Texas to be free from Mexico.

Some American place names seem to have no special history. The names of towns like *Polka Dot* (Ohio), *Sleepy Eye* (Minnesota), and *Frostproof* (Florida) may have been made up just for fun!

Think about the information story. Read over your chart. Then answer the questions.

1. Use your chart. How did some animals get their names?

2. Use your chart. What is special about the sunflower's name?

3. What might a place name tell you about that place's history?

4. Why do you think some places are named for famous people?

5. Imagine you live in a town with a name like Polka Dot. How might you feel about the name and why?

6. Why does this information story belong in a unit about telling names?

Choose three animals. Think of new names for these animals. The names should describe the animals. You might decide to call a camel a *mountainback.* Talk about the new names you choose. Ask questions about what each person says.

WORK IN A GROUP

Learn About

PICTURES IN BOOKS
Illustrators and Illustrations

When you choose a book, do you read the words or look at the pictures first? Many people like to turn the pages and look at the pictures. If they like the pictures, they may be interested in reading the words.

In a picture book the pictures help to tell the story. They show you how the people and the places look, and what is happening. The pictures also show the story's feeling, or *mood.* The pictures tell you if a story is funny, frightening, or sad. Pictures may help you catch the feeling of poems, too.

The people who make the pictures in a book are called *illustrators.* Each illustrator has a special way of creating pictures. On the next pages you will learn about three illustrators and their different ways of working.

228

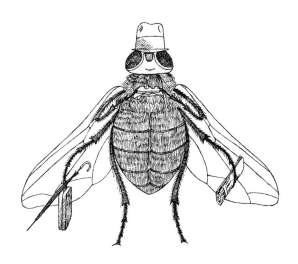

From the poem "The Fly in Rye"
by N. M. Bodecker

N. M. Bodecker likes to illustrate his
poems with unusual drawings. His poems make
you laugh, and his drawings—a fly, a cherry,
or a pickle dressed in clothing—are funny to see.

N. M. Bodecker's drawings show that
lines can do many things. See what thin lines
he used to show how light the fly's wings are.
Look at the short, thin lines he used to draw
the fly's fuzzy body and legs. For its eyes, he
used *crosshatching.* He made a set of lines
and then crossed them with another set.

From the story *Stevie*
by John Steptoe

The bold, heavy lines in this picture should catch your attention. Follow the lines around the picture. See how the lines form a circle that brings the mother and her son close together. John Steptoe, the author and illustrator, wants you to feel the love between mother and son. The picture, rather than the words, tells how they feel.

Notice how the bright colors in this picture may *overlap,* or flow one over the other. Look for the overlapping colors on the table.

This illustration was cut from a single piece of paper. Illustrations made this way are called *paper cuts.* Ed Young used this Chinese art form to illustrate *The Emperor and the Kite.* Paper cuts are made with tools that press straight down onto the paper to cut the shapes. Drops of dye are put on the paper to make the blended colors.

In this picture Ed Young helps you feel the excitement of the emperor climbing the rope. The emperor's robes fly out like wings. Imagine how hard it was to cut the emperor's robes.

From the Chinese folk tale *The Emperor and the Kite* retold by Jane Yolen

Now choose a story and illustrate your favorite part. Will you use crayon, paint, or cut paper? Try to catch the story's mood in your picture.

You have read these selections.

Rumpelstiltskin
Paper Boats *and* **Oliphaunt**
Rufus M.
The Naming of Olga da Polga
Names and Their Meanings

Talk about the selections. Talk about how the ideas and characters are alike and different. Talk about the theme.

1. How are Rumpelstiltskin and Olga da Polga alike? How are they different?

2. How are Rufus M. and Olga da Polga alike? How are they different?

3. Pretend that Rufus is named Rumpelstiltskin. What might happen in "Rufus M."?

4. In which selection are names the most important? Why do you think as you do?

BOOKSHELF

Koko's Story by Dr. Francine Patterson. Scholastic, 1987. Koko, a gorilla, learns sign language to name what she wants.

Whose Cat Is That? by Virginia Kahl. Charles Scribner's, 1979. A small white cat wants to find a home but instead finds seven. Now she has to pretend to be seven cats with seven different names.

I Have Four Names for My Grandfather by Kathryn Lasky. Little, Brown, 1976. A grandfather is a special person to this young boy.

In a Pickle and Other Funny Idioms by Marvin Terban. Clarion Books, 1983. This book explains why we say that we "let the cat out of the bag" or that we "got it straight from the horse's mouth" and other sayings.

Thumbelina by Hans Christian Andersen. Dial Books, 1979. A girl no bigger than your thumb is named Thumbelina. Though small, she has many big adventures.

4 You Can't Catch Me

Look at the picture on pages 234 and 235. Read the title.

1. When have you heard someone say, "You can't catch me"?

2. What is happening in the picture?

3. Who in the picture might be saying, "You can't catch me"?

4. How do you think the boy in the picture feels?

5. You will read some selections. How do you think the selections will be alike?

Other Books About Escaping

Where the Buffaloes Begin by Olaf Baker. Frederick Warne, 1981. An Indian boy risks his life to save his people from enemy attack.

Dancing Turtle by Maggie Duff. Macmillan, 1981. This Louisiana folk tale tells about a turtle who outwits a raccoon to save her own life.

Focusing on "Dance of the Animals"

Think and Read

▶ Talk about things people do to feel better when they are sad. Ask your classmates questions.

▶ Look at the title and the picture on page 238. Think about what you know about being sad.
  • Who seems sad in this play?
  • What might the characters do to feel better? Why do you think that?

▶ Get ready to read about some animal characters. As you read, think about the tricks that the animals play. Think about how to complete this chart.

Who plans the trick?	What is the trick?	How well does the trick work?

Now turn the page and read "Dance of the Animals." Then you will talk about clever tricks.

Dance of the Animals

A play adapted from a Puerto Rican folk tale retold by Pura Belpré
Pictures by Willi K. Baum

Glossary of Spanish Words

amiga mía (ah·MEE·gah MEE·ah) My friend.
amigo (ah·MEE·goh) Friend.
buenos días (BWAY·nohs THEE·ahs) Good day.
gracias (GRAH·see·ahs) Thank you.
hola (OH·lah) Hello.
jotas (HOH·tahs) Traditional Spanish dances.
señor (sen·YOHR) Sir, mister.
señora (sen·YOHR·ah) Lady, madam.
sí (SEE) Yes.

Characters

Narrator 1	Señor Lion	Señor Dog
Narrator 2	Señora Lioness	Señora Dog
Narrator 3	Señora Mare	Señor Goat
Narrator 4	Señora Donkey	

Setting: In the forest.

SCENE ONE

Narrator 1: Once upon a time, a lion and a lioness lived together near a great forest. Among their neighbors were Señor Horse and Señora Mare, Señor and Señora Donkey, Señor Bull and Señora Cow, Señor and Señora Dog, and Señor and Señora Goat.

Times were hard for Señor Lion and Señora Lioness, and soon the day came when they faced each other with nothing to fix for a meal.

Señora Lioness: We must do something. If times keep up like this, we shall certainly die. We cannot let that happen, for are we not the strongest beasts in the forest? Has it not been said that the bigger fish shall eat the smaller?

Señor Lion: True enough. Something must be done.

Narrator 1: Señor Lion set to thinking for a while. A short time later, an idea came to him.

Señor Lion: I have it. And a splendid idea it is, even if I have to say it myself. Listen. Which meat do we like the best?

Señora Lioness: Goat's meat.

Señor Lion: Right. It is the finest, the juiciest and certainly the tastiest. Ah, *Señora mía,* you shall see.

Señora Lioness: But how are we going to get such fresh and delicious meat?

Señor Lion: I will tell you. Listen carefully. We shall give a ball—a grand ball. And we shall invite our friends to come to it. You, who are so well liked, will ask our neighbors, and they will not refuse. We will build a roasting pit. Everyone will be dancing. And when the goats get close to the pit, I will push them into the hot coals. The rest depends on me. How do you like my plan?

Narrator 1: Señora Lioness thought for a while, at first shaking her head slowly as if the plan did not meet with her approval. Then suddenly she realized what it meant.

Señora Lioness: What a good idea! Meat at last.

Señor Lion: You will have to hurry if my plans are to be carried out.

Narrator 1: Señora Lioness went out to invite the neighbors, while Señor Lion stayed home to prepare for the big affair.

SCENE TWO

Señora Lioness: *Hola!* Señora Mare!

Señora Mare: *Hola!* Señora Lioness. What are you doing around these parts, my good friend?

Señora Lioness: I came to invite you to a dance. You and Señor Horse have such fine long legs and such strong hoofs. We need you for our orchestra. Could you not come and play the drum?

Señora Mare: Oh, most certainly. Only yesterday was I saying that we needed a little recreation. Yes, we will come and play the drum.

Señora Lioness: *Gracias.*

Narrator 2: And Señora Lioness went on her way. Pretty soon she found Señora Donkey.

Señora Lioness: Ah, *amiga mía.* I was coming to see you. We are giving a ball and would like to have you and Señor Donkey come. Señor Horse and Señora Mare are coming to play the drum. Won't you and Señor Donkey come and play the trombone?

Señora Donkey: Why, yes, Señora Lioness, we will be there without fail.

Señora Lioness: *Gracias, gracias.*

Narrator 2: On went Señora Lioness, faster and faster as she felt the pangs of hunger in her empty stomach. She had not had goat's meat in such a long time. She crossed lane after lane inviting more and more neighbors. She gave each invitation with such graciousness that those invited felt that the dance would not be a success unless they accepted.

Señora Lioness found Señor and Señora Dog sitting under the shade of a great tree. She greeted them a little breathless, for she had walked quite a distance now.

Señora Lioness: *Hola, amigos.* There is a great ball at our place tonight. You must both come.

Señor Dog: I will go, but Señora Dog stays home.

Señora Dog: I will go, too.

Señor Dog: No! No!

Señora Dog: *Sí! Sí!*

Señora Lioness: Oh, my friends, I must leave you to decide the matter yourselves. I must call on Señor Goat.

Señor Dog: Wait, Señora Lioness. Señor Goat is my best friend. I will take you to him.

Narrator 2: Once at Señor Goat's place, Señor Dog took him aside and suggested that he go alone to the dance. Señor Goat agreed.

Señor Dog: Señora Lioness, thank you for your kind invitation. Señor Goat and I will gladly come. The Señoras, however, will stay home.

Narrator 2: Señora Lioness left with a sad heart, for Señor Goat would not provide enough meat for two.

Señora Lioness (*To herself*): Oh, what will Señor Lion say when he learns that only Señor Goat is coming? Señor Goat is so small and thin.

Scene Three

Narrator 3: Señora Lioness soon reached home. Señor Lion had dug a roasting pit in which hot coals burned brightly.

Señor Lion: Well, you are here at last. Are they all coming?

Señora Lioness: Yes, all—that is, except. . . .

Narrator 3: Señora Lioness never finished the sentence, for so excited was Señor Lion that he danced for joy and then went to tend the fire. Señora Lioness had hardly finished putting on her garland of flowers when the first guests arrived.

Señor Lion: *Buenos días,* Señor and Señora Donkey.

Señora Donkey: What a beautiful garland! And how becoming.

Señora Lioness: *Gracias,* my friend.

Narrator 3: More guests arrived, all clean and looking their very best. Señora Cat had woven a bunch of honeysuckle on a blue ribbon around her neck. Señor Bull and Señora Cow had threaded grey and red wreaths around their horns. Last came Señor Dog and Señor Goat. Señor Lion greeted them.

Señor Lion: And where are the Señoras? Aren't they coming?

Señor Goat: No.

Señor Dog: Oh, no.

Narrator 3: Señor Lion leaned over and whispered to his wife.

Señor Lion: My dear, we shall have to eat them both, since Señora Goat did not come.

247

Narrator 3: Señor Lion and Señora Lioness opened
the dance. The couples whirled, stamped, and
bellowed. What tangos and *jotas!* Waltzes
mixed with mazurkas and traditional dances.

What a mixture of sounds! Señor Dog
barked and howled. Señor and Señora Cat
meowed, while the constant stamping of Señor
Donkey and the brays of Señora Mare filled the
place.

Suddenly on one of the turns of the dance
Señor Goat and Señor Dog spied the fire
in the pit.

Señor Goat: *Amigo*, I do not like the look of that fire. Let us go, for this fire is meant for us. No doubt, Señor Lion means to eat us.

Narrator 3: Then, through the dancers they pulled and pushed, skipping all the time until they reached the woods.

Señor Dog: Hurry, *amigo!* Now we must run just as fast as we possibly can.

Narrator 3: Meanwhile, at the ball things went on as before. Suddenly Señor Lion missed Señor Dog and Señor Goat. As quickly as he could without causing suspicion, he left and followed Señor Dog's and Señor Goat's trail.

SCENE FOUR

Narrator 4: The afternoon was cool and the air was heavy with the scent of the acacia trees in full bloom. The wind began to blow and with it came rain, slowly at first and then in great torrents. The river soon was swollen with the sudden downpour.

Señor Dog: *Amigo,* I am going to swim across the river. Come! Follow me.

Señor Goat (*To himself, as he stands by the bank of the river*): Señor Lion will soon be here and I cannot swim. Oh, for a good safe hiding place! Ah, perhaps I can hide in that stack of hay.

Narrator 4: No sooner had Señor Goat hidden himself and Señor Dog made his way across the river, then Señor Lion appeared. On the other side of the river, Señor Dog stood, happily jumping around and mocking Señor Lion.

Señor Lion (*Picking up and throwing a large stone*): Watch out, Señor Dog!

Señor Dog: Oh, my friend, see that bundle of straw near you? Why don't you try to throw a piece of that at me?

Señor Lion: One piece, indeed. I will throw the whole stack at you.

Narrator 4: And Señor Lion leaned forward and tried to pick up the heavy bundle of hay. But he only slipped and fell on his back. At this Señor Dog leaped up and barked for joy.

Señor Dog: Try again, my friend.

Narrator 4: Señor Lion got up and tugged at the straw bundle again. He pulled and pulled and finally managed to lift it and hurl it across the river. No sooner did it land on the ground than Señor Goat jumped out of his hiding place. And accompanied by Señor Dog, he began to leap joyfully in the air.

Señor Goat: Señor Lion, thanks for helping me over. If I did lose most of my tail, my life, indeed, I saved.

Narrator 4: Señor Lion's rage had no limit and, looking down at his paws, he discovered that he had a large amount of fur entangled in his claws. Then he laughed.

Señor Lion: So you have, my friend, but by your stump you'll tell your tale.

Narrator 4: And it is true, because even to this day most goats have only a stump for a tail.

About

For a long time, folk tales all over the world have been passed down by storytellers. A storyteller of our own time is Pura Belpré (PAW•rah BEL•pray), who tells the folk tales she heard as a child in Puerto Rico.

While working in the New York Public Library, Pura Belpré told folk tales to children. To make her stories more lively, she began making and using puppets. When people wanted to read the folk tales, Pura Belpré wrote them down. Though many of the stories are in books now, she still likes to tell the tales with her handmade puppets.

More Books by Pura Belpré

The Rainbow-Colored Horse
Perez and Martina
The Tiger and the Rabbit

Think about the play. Copy the chart on page 237. Fill in the information. Then answer the questions.

1. Use your chart. Who plays the best trick? Tell why you think so.

2. A grand ball is an important part of Señor Lion's plan. Why do you think he decides to give a party?

3. Señor Dog knows there might be a trick even before he gets to the party. How do you know that?

4. Suppose Señor Goat had gone alone to the party. What trick could he have used to escape on his own?

5. Think about why this play is a *why* story. What does it explain?

6. Who in the play might say "You can't catch me"? Why do you think that?

Tell about other story characters who play tricks on each other. Ask questions about what your classmates say. Talk about the answers.

WORK IN A GROUP

Focusing on "The Grasshopper" and "Not Me"

Think and Read

▶ Sometimes it is fun to just be silly. Talk about some silly things you have done. Ask your classmates questions about what they say.

▶ Read the titles on pages 257 and 260. Look at the pictures that go with these poems.
- Will the poems be serious or silly? Tell why you think so.
- Which poem might be sillier? Why?
- What do you think will happen in "The Grasshopper"?

▶ Get ready to read two poems. As you read, notice how each poem begins and ends. Think about how you would fill in this chart.

Poem	How It Begins	How It Ends
"The Grasshopper"		
"Not Me"		

Now turn the page and read "The Grasshopper" and "Not Me." Then you will talk about silly poems.

256

The Grasshopper

A poem by David McCord

Down

a

deep

well

a

grasshopper

fell.

By kicking about

He thought to get out.

He might have known better,

For that got him wetter.

Pictures by Julie Peterson

To kick round and round
Is the way to get drowned,
    And drowning is what
    I should tell you he got.
        But
        the
        well
        had
        a
        rope
        that
        dangled
        some
        hope.

And sure as molasses
On one of his passes
    He found the rope handy
    And up he went, *and he*
        it
        up
        and
        it
        up
        and
        it
        up
        and
        it
        up
        went
And hopped away proper
As any grasshopper.

Not Me

A poem by Shel Silverstein

The Slithergadee has crawled out of the sea.
He may catch all the others, but he
    won't catch me.
No, you won't catch me, Old Slithergadee,
You may catch all the others, but you wo—

Picture by Robert Evans

261

Think about the poems. Copy the chart on page 256. Fill in the information. Then answer the questions.

Copy the chart on page 256.

Think and Discuss

1. Use your chart. What problem does the grasshopper have? Is it a serious or a silly problem? Why?

2. Use your chart. How are the endings of the two poems different? Which one is sillier?

3. Why does "Not Me" end in the middle of a word? What is the speaker going to say? How does this make the poem silly?

4. How would you have ended the poem "Not Me"? Why?

5. What is unusual about how some of the words on page 258 are written? How does this make the poem silly?

the words on page 258

6. Why does each poem belong in a unit about not catching things?

WORK IN A GROUP

Tell what makes someone do silly things. Ask questions about what your classmates say. Talk about the answers.

Focusing on "The Emperor and the Kite"

▶ Talk about how people have shown they are loyal, or true, to you. Ask your classmates questions about what they say.

▶ Read the title on page 264. Look at the picture on page 265. Also read page 264. Think about what you know about loyalty.
  - Who will the main characters be?
  - What is happening in the picture?
  - What might happen in this story?

▶ Get ready to read about a young princess. As you read, think about how she solves two problems. Think about how to fill in this chart.

Main Character	
Setting	
First Problem	Second Problem
How It Is Solved	How It Is Solved

Now turn the page and read "The Emperor and the Kite." Then you will talk about loyalty.

The Emperor and the Kite

A Chinese folk tale retold by Jane Yolen
Pictures by Ed Young

The ancient sport of kite flying began long ago in China. No one knows for certain when or where in China kites were invented, and no one knows who flew the first one.

Kites are found in many old Chinese folk tales. In this folk tale, a stick-and-paper kite is the favorite toy of a lonely Emperor's daughter named Djeow Seow (jeeOH seeOW).

Once in ancient China there lived a princess who was the fourth daughter of the emperor. She was very tiny. In fact she was so tiny her name was Djeow Seow, which means "the smallest one." And, because she was so tiny, she was not thought very much of—when she was thought of at all.

265

Her brothers, who were all older and bigger and stronger than she, were thought of all the time. And they were like four rising suns in the eyes of their father.

Her three sisters were all older and bigger and stronger than she. They were like three midnight moons in the eyes of their father.

But Djeow Seow was like a tiny star in the emperor's sight. The emperor often forgot he had a fourth daughter at all.

Every morning, when the wind came from the east past the rising sun, Djeow Seow flew her kite. And every evening, when the wind went to the west past the setting sun, she flew her kite. Her toy was like a flower in the sky.

A monk who passed the palace every day made up a poem about her kite.

My kite sails upward,
Mounting to the high heavens.
My soul goes on wings.

Each day Princess Djeow Seow thanked him for his poem. Then she went back to flying her kite.

But just as the wind is not always peaceful, all was not peaceful in the kingdom. There were evil men plotting against the emperor. They crept up on him one day when he was alone. Only Princess Djeow Seow saw what happened.

The evil men took the emperor to a tower in the middle of a wide, treeless plain. The tower had only a single window. The men sealed the door with bricks and mortar. Then they rode back to the palace and said that the emperor was dead.

When his sons and daughters heard this, they ran away. But Djeow Seow built a hut of twigs and branches at the edge of the plain.

Every day at dawn and again at dark, she would walk across the plain to the tower. And there she would sail her stick-and-paper kite. To the kite string she tied a tiny basket filled with rice and poppyseed cakes, water chestnuts and green tea. The kite pulled the basket high, high in the air, up as high as the window in the tower. And, in this way, she kept her father alive.

So they lived for many days.

The evil men were cruel, and the people of the country were very sad.

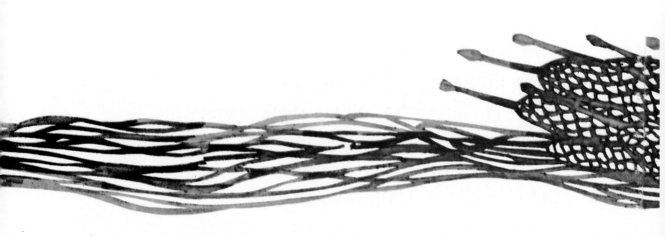

One day, as the princess prepared a basket of food for her father, the old monk passed by her hut. She smiled at him, but he seemed not to see her.

Yet, as he passed, he repeated his poem in a loud voice. He said:

> *My kite sails upward,*
> *Mounting to the high heavens.*
> *My emperor goes on wings.*

The princess started to thank him. But then she stopped. Something was different. The words were not quite right.

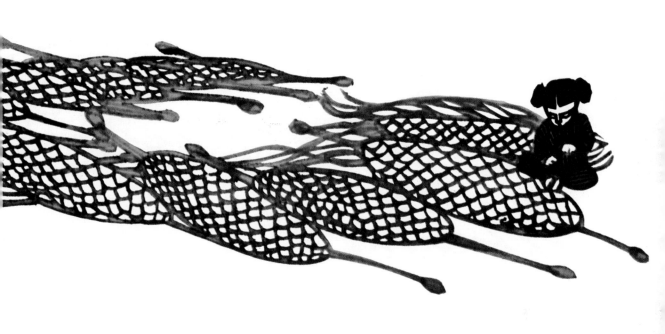

And then Djeow Seow understood. The
monk was telling her something important.

Each day after that, Djeow Seow was
busy. She twined a string of grass and
vines, and wove in strands of her own long
black hair. When her rope was as thick as
her waist and as high as the tower, she was
ready. She attached the rope to the string
of the stick-and-paper kite, and made her
way across the treeless plain.

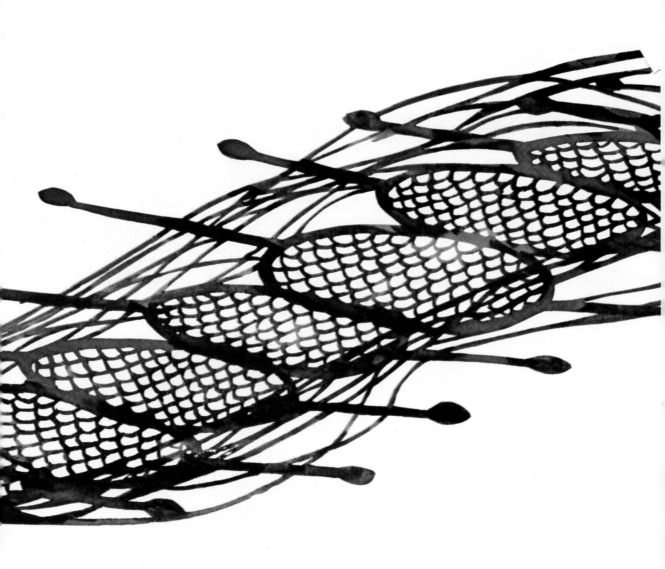

When she reached the tower, she called
to her father. But her voice was as tiny as
she, and her words were lost in the wind.

At last, though, the emperor looked out and saw his daughter flying her kite. He expected the tiny basket of food to sail up to his window as it had done each day. But what should he see but the strand of vines and grass and long black hair. The wind was raging above, holding the kite in its steely grip. And the princess was below, holding tight to the end of the rope.

The emperor leaned out of the tower window and grasped the heavy strand. He brought it into his tower room and loosened the string of the kite. He set the kite free.

Then the emperor tied one end of the thick strand to the heavy iron bar across the window, and the other end stretched all the way down to Djeow Seow's tiny hands.

The emperor stepped to the window sill and slid down the rope. His robes billowed out around him like the wings of a bright kite.

When his feet reached the ground, he knelt before his tiny daughter. And he touched the ground before her with his lips. Then he rose and embraced her, and she almost disappeared in his arms.

He lifted the tiny princess to his shoulders and carried her all the way back to the palace.

At the palace, the emperor was greeted by wild and cheering crowds. The people were tired of the evil men, but they had been afraid to act. With the emperor once again to guide them, they threw the evil men into prison.

And when the other sons and daughters of the emperor heard of his return, they hurried home to welcome their father. When they arrived, they were surprised to find Djeow Seow on a tiny throne by their father's side.

To the end of his days, the emperor ruled with Princess Djeow Seow close by.

And, too, it is said that Djeow Seow
ruled after him, as gentle as the wind and,
in her loyalty, as unyielding.

About
ED YOUNG

Do you ever daydream? When Ed Young was a boy in China, he daydreamed so much that his mother wondered what would become of him. The rest of the family, however, enjoyed the plays and the drawings Ed Young made up from his dreams.

Ed Young came to the United States to go to art school. *The Mean Mouse and Other Mean Stories* was the first book he illustrated. Since then, he has become well known as an illustrator who uses modern forms of ancient arts. In *The Emperor and the Kite,* he used the Chinese art of paper cutting.

More Books Illustrated by Ed Young

Bicycle Rider
The Girl Who Loved the Wind
The Red Lion: A Persian Story
The Rooster's Horns: A Chinese Puppet Play to
    Make and Perform
The Lion and the Mouse

Think about the story. Copy the story plan on page 263. Fill in the information. Then answer the questions.

1. Use your story plan. What problems does Djeow Seow solve? What does this tell you about her?

2. Look at your story plan. Who in the story might say, "You can't catch me"? Tell why you think as you do.

3. How does the monk show his loyalty to the emperor?

4. Think about Djeow Seow's loyalty to the emperor. How is it different from the loyalty of the other characters?

5. With what moral, or lesson, could this folk tale end?

6. The emperor shows he is thankful to Djeow Seow. How does he show he is loyal to her?

Tell how what happened to the emperor changed his ideas. Ask questions about what your classmates say. Talk about the answers.

WORK IN A GROUP

Peter and the Wolf *by Sergei Prokofiev*

In some stories the characters get into trouble. They need a way to get out of that trouble. They need a "great escape" plan. Sometimes the characters think of their own "great escape" plans. Sometimes someone else helps them escape. In the story above, who helps the cat and the bird escape from the wolf?

The characters in the stories below all had "great escape" plans. Choose one or both of these stories. Tell what the plans were by answering the questions.

1. **Dance of the Animals**

   Who was in trouble?
   How did they escape?
   Who helped them escape?

2. **The Emperor and the Kite**

   Who was in trouble?
   How did he escape?
   Who helped him escape?

Now you be the author. The character in this picture is in trouble. Draw or tell a story about her "great escape" plan. Write a title for your story. Begin by telling *who* the character is and *how* her trouble began. Then tell *how* she escaped.

Focusing on "The Cat Came Back"

▶ Have you ever had a pet that caused problems? Talk about when a pet was a problem. Ask your classmates questions.

▶ Read the title of the song on page 286. Look at the picture on page 287. Think about what you know about pets.
  • What do you think is happening?
  • Will this song be funny or serious? What makes you think so?

▶ Get ready to read a song about a cat who keeps coming back. As you read, think of all the things that happen to the cat. Think about how to complete this chart.

What things should make the cat disappear?	What happens instead?
1. 2. 3.	

Now turn the page and read "The Cat Came Back." Then you will talk about not giving up.

The Cat Came Back

A folk song adapted by Dahlov Ipcar

There was an old yellow cat
    had troubles all her own.
No one seemed to want her,
    but she wouldn't leave her home.
They tried everything they knew
    to drive that cat away.
They took her to Alaska,
    and they told her for to stay—

BUT

The cat came back,
She couldn't stay no longer.
The cat came back,
'Cause she couldn't stay away.
The cat came back,
We thought she was a goner,
But the cat came back

ON THE VERY NEXT DAY!

Pictures by Julie Peterson

287

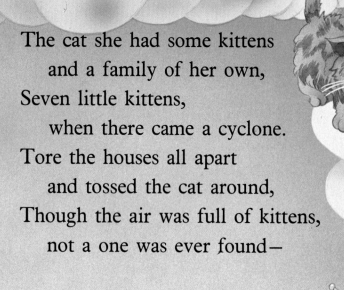

The cat she had some kittens
    and a family of her own,
Seven little kittens,
    when there came a cyclone.
Tore the houses all apart
    and tossed the cat around,
Though the air was full of kittens,
    not a one was ever found—

BUT

The cat came back,
She couldn't stay no longer.
The cat came back,
'Cause she couldn't stay away.
The cat came back,
We thought she was a goner,
But the cat came back

ON THE VERY NEXT DAY!

Then they took her to Cape Canaveral
    and found that cat a place
Right inside a rocket
    that was heading into space.
They thought that when she reached the moon,
    they'd really have it made,
But the cat returned in triumph
    for a ticker tape parade!

Oh, the cat came back!
She couldn't stay no longer.
The cat came back,
'Cause she couldn't stay away.
The cat came back,
We thought she was a goner,
But the cat came back

ON THE VERY NEXT DAY!

Think about the song. Copy the chart on page 285. Fill in the information. Then answer the questions.

1. Use your chart. What bad things happen to the cat? What does the cat do?

2. Why does the cat keep coming back?

3. Do you feel sorrier for the cat or its owners? Why?

4. From what other adventure might the cat come back?

5. The main character of this song is a cat. Could this song have been about another animal? Why or why not?

6. How is the cat like Olga da Polga?

7. Why does this song belong in a unit about not catching something?

WORK IN A GROUP

Tell about why both animals and people sometimes do not give up. Ask your classmates whether they think not giving up is good or bad. Talk about the answers.

Focusing on "Animal Travelers"

▶ Have you ever seen groups of birds flying together? Talk about what you know about birds that fly in groups. Ask questions.

▶ Read the title and the poem on page 292. Then look at the pictures in the story.
  • What is the topic of this story?
  • Do you think the article will only be about geese? Why or why not?
  • Will this story be fiction or nonfiction? How do you know?

▶ Get ready to read an information story about some animals that travel every year. Find out how they travel and where they go. Copy this chart and make notes on it as you read.

Animals	How They Travel	In What Direction
1.		
2.		

Now turn the page and read "Animal Travelers."
Then you will talk about animals that travel.

Animal Travelers

Something told the wild geese
   It was time to go.
Though the fields lay golden
   Something whispered, "Snow."
     • • •
Something told the wild geese
   It was time to fly—
Summer sun was on their wings,
   Winter in their cry.
        —Rachel Field

Summer is over in the northern part of
the world. The days are getting shorter.
The weather is cooler. It is time for many
animals to be on the move. They must
head south now to escape the harsh winter
that lies ahead.

Flocks of *Canada geese* gather at their
nesting places. They circle in the air. Then
they fly south. Some will fly as far south
as Mexico. When snow falls in the north,
the geese will be settled in their warm,
winter homes. They will be able to find
food all winter.

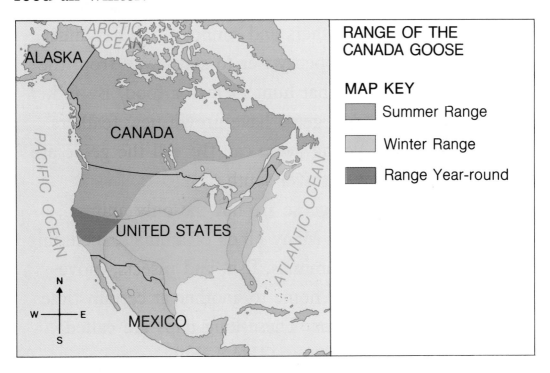

293

The geese will return in the spring. They will fly back to their nesting places, where they will lay their eggs and raise their young. The geese return north to raise their families because summer days are longer there. Parent geese need the extra hours of daylight to find food for their hungry babies.

In summer the adult geese lose their flight feathers and cannot fly. They must keep to open water to stay away from the animals that hunt them for food. By fall, the adult geese have grown new feathers. The young geese can fly. All the geese are ready to travel south.

Wild geese are not the only animal travelers. Many kinds of animals, including birds, mammals, fish, and insects, move from one home to another at certain times of the year. These long trips are called *migrations* (my•GRAY•shunz).

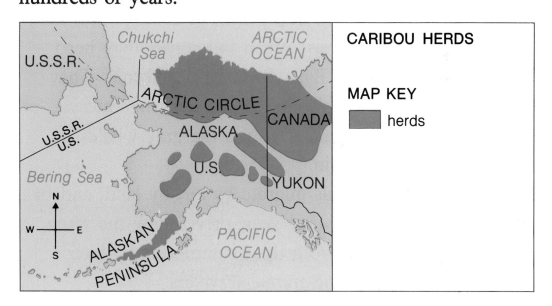

The longest migrations on land are made by members of the deer family. *Caribou* (KAIR·ih·boo) live in the Arctic. In the fall they gather in herds of thousands of animals. Then they move south to find food. Caribou travel up to eight hundred miles from their summer homes. In spring they return north. They follow routes caribou have taken for hundreds of years.

CARIBOU HERDS

MAP KEY

herds

The world's largest migrators travel through the seas. They are the *whales.* The map shows the migration path of the California gray whale. Each year gray whales make a round trip of eight thousand miles.

In summer the whales stay near Alaska, where they find plenty of food—crabs, fish, and shrimps. When fall comes they head south, to Baja (BAH•ha) California. They have their young in these warm waters. When summer comes the gray whales go north again.

Animals migrate by air, by land, and by sea. Year after year, they follow the same paths between their summer and winter homes—the animal travelers.

Think about the information story. Read over your chart. Then answer the questions.

1. Use your chart. In what direction do the three animals travel in the winter? Why do they each travel in the same direction?

2. Many animals migrate to warmer places in winter. Why do they not stay there all year?

3. What is a danger that these animals might face as they come south?

4. If you could migrate, to what place would you go? Why?

5. Groups of animals go to the same places each year. How do you think they know where to go?

6. Why does this information story belong in a unit about not catching things?

Talk to one another about why people move. Think about whether animals move for the same reasons. Ask questions about what your classmates say. Talk about the answers.

Think and Discuss

WORK IN A GROUP

You have read these selections.

Dance of the Animals
The Grasshopper *and* **Not Me**
The Emperor and the Kite
The Cat Came Back
Animal Travelers

Talk about the selections. Talk about how the ideas and characters are alike and different. Talk about the theme.

1. How are Señor Dog and Señor Goat and the animals in "Animal Travelers" alike? How are they different?

2. How are the escapes of Señor Goat and the emperor alike?

3. How are the animals in "Animal Travelers" and the cat in "The Cat Came Back" alike?

4. Which selection tells about the best escape? Why do you think as you do?

BOOKSHELF

Nora's Castle by Satomi Ichikawa. Philomel, 1986. A girl, accompanied by her doll, her teddy bear, and her dog, goes to find out who lives in the mysterious castle on the hill.

Wiley and the Hairy Man by Molly Garrett Bang. Macmillan, 1976. When Wiley goes out on the Tombigbee River, he meets the Hairy Man. Wiley must find a way to escape.

The Angry Moon by William Sleator. Little, Brown, 1970. Lupan climbs into the sky on an arrow ladder to try to rescue his friend from the angry moon.

Petronella by Jay Williams. Parents Magazine Press, 1973. Like her two brothers, Petronella sets out on an adventure. She, however, is looking for a prince to rescue.

The Three Wishes: A Collection of Puerto Rican Folktales retold by Ricardo E. Alegría. Harcourt Brace Jovanovich, 1969. Princesses and clever animals escape from danger in these fine tales.

5 Would You Believe It!

TALKING ABOUT THE THEME

Look at the picture on pages 300 and 301.
Read the title.

1. What is happening in the picture?

2. Is what is happening believable? Why do you think as you do?

3. How does this picture make you feel?

4. What kinds of things are you most likely to believe?

5. You will read some selections. How do you think the selections will be alike?

Other Books About Unbelievable Things

The Banza by Diane Wolkstein. Dial Books, 1981. A special banza, or bango, protects a goat during the goat's adventures.

Mother Crocodile: An Amadou Tale from Senegal by Birago Diop, translated by Rosa Guy. Delacorte, 1981. A storyteller from Senegal tells a tale about a mother crocodile who tries to share her wisdom with young crocodiles.

Focusing on "Talk"

▶ Talk about stories you have read that are about make-believe people and things. Ask questions about what your classmates say.

▶ Look at the title on page 305 and the pictures on pages 304–312. Think about what you know about make-believe stories.
- What do you think is happening?
- Where do you think this story takes place? How do you know?

▶ Get ready to read a story about a farmer. As you read, think about what happens that is make-believe. Think about what to list on this chart.

What Is Make-believe in the Story

Now turn the page and read "Talk." Then you will talk about make-believe things.

Talk

A West African folk tale retold by Harold Courlander and George Herzog
Pictures by Sarn Suvityasiri

Once, not far from the city of Accra on the
Gulf of Guinea, a country man went out to his
garden to dig up some yams to take to market.
While he was digging, one of the yams said to
him:

"Well, at last you're here. You never
weeded me, but now you come around with
your digging stick. Go away and leave me
alone!"

The farmer turned around and looked at his
cow in amazement. The cow was chewing her
cud and looking at him.

"Did you say something?" he asked.

The cow kept on chewing and said nothing, but the man's dog spoke up.

"It wasn't the cow who spoke to you," the dog said. "It was the yam. The yam says to leave him alone."

The man became angry, because his dog had never talked before, and he didn't like his tone besides. So he took his knife and cut a branch from a palm tree to whip his dog. Just then the palm tree said:

"Put that branch down!"

The man was getting very upset about the way things were going, and he started to throw the palm branch away, but the palm branch said:

"Man, put me down softly!"

He put the branch down gently on a stone, and the stone said:

"Hey, take that thing off me!"

This was enough, and the frightened farmer started to run for his village. On the way he met a fisherman going the other way with a fish trap on his head.

"What's the hurry?" the fisherman asked.

"My yam said, 'Leave me alone!' Then the
dog said, 'Listen to what the yam says!' When
I went to whip the dog with a palm branch the
tree said, 'Put that branch down!' Then the
palm branch said, 'Do it softly!' Then the stone
said, 'Take that thing off me!'"

"Is that all?" the man with the fish trap
asked. "Is that so frightening?"

"Well," the man's fish trap said, "did he
take it off the stone?"

"Wah!" the fisherman shouted. He threw
the fish trap on the ground and began to run
with the farmer, and on the trail they met a
weaver with a bundle of cloth on his head.

"Where are you going in such a rush?" he asked them.

"My yam said, 'Leave me alone!'" the farmer said. "The dog said, 'Listen to what the yam says!' The tree said, 'Put that branch down!' The branch said, 'Do it softly!' And the stone said, 'Take that thing off me!'"

"And then," the fisherman continued, "the fish trap said, 'Did he take it off?'"

"That's nothing to get excited about," the weaver said, "no reason at all."

"Oh yes it is," his bundle of cloth said. "If it happened to you you'd run too!"

"Wah!" the weaver shouted. He threw his bundle on the trail and started running with the other men.

They came panting to the ford in the river
and found a man bathing.

"Are you chasing a gazelle?" he asked them.

The first man said breathlessly:

"My yam talked at me, and it said, 'Leave
me alone!' And my dog said, 'Listen to your
yam!' And when I cut myself a branch the tree
said, 'Put that branch down!' And the branch
said, 'Do it softly!' And the stone said, 'Take
that thing off me!'"

The fisherman panted:

"And my trap said, 'Did he?'"

The weaver wheezed:

"And my bundle of cloth said, 'You'd run too!'"

"Is that why you're running?" the man in the river asked.

"Well, wouldn't you run if you were in their position?" the river said.

The man jumped out of the water and began to run with the others. They ran down the main street of the village to the house of the chief. The chief's servants brought his stool out, and he came and sat on it to listen to their complaints. The men began to recite their troubles.

"I went out to my garden to dig yams," the farmer said, waving his arms. "Then everything began to talk! My yam said, 'Leave me alone!' My dog said, 'Pay attention to your yam!' The tree said, 'Put that branch down!' The branch said, 'Do it softly!' And the stone said, 'Take it off me!'"

"And my fish trap said, 'Well, did he take it off?'" the fisherman said.

"And my cloth said, 'You'd run too!'" the weaver said.

"And the river said the same," the bather said hoarsely, his eyes bulging.

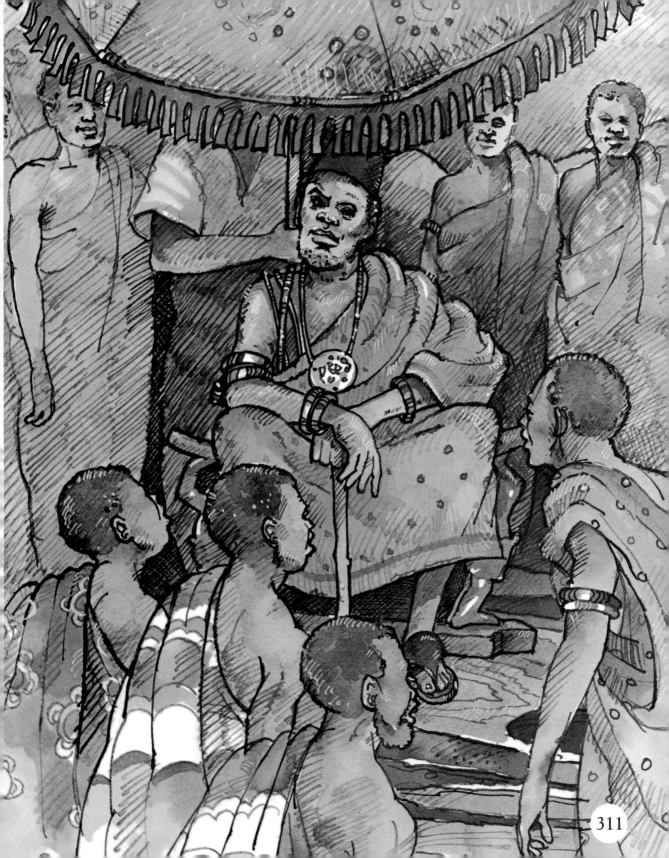

The chief listened to them patiently, but he couldn't refrain from scowling.

"Now this is really a wild story," he said at last. "You'd better all go back to your work before I punish you for disturbing the peace."

So the men went away, and the chief shook his head and mumbled to himself, "Nonsense like that upsets the community."

"Fantastic, isn't it?" his stool said. "Imagine, a talking yam!"

Think about the story. Copy the chart on page 303. Fill in the information. Then answer the questions.

1. Use your chart. Also, think about what you know about things that are make-believe. At first, why does the farmer think his cow has spoken rather than the yam?

2. Use your chart. Why is the farmer angry at his dog?

3. Suppose the fish trap did not speak. Would the fisherman still be upset by the farmer's story? Tell why you think as you do.

4. Why do you think the chief believes the villagers are telling him a wild story? What happens to change the chief's mind?

5. Why do you think the writer has the chief's stool speak?

6. How would you change this story so that it would not belong in a unit about unbelievable things?

Discuss why someone might tell the story "Talk." Ask questions about what your classmates say. Talk about the answers.

WORK IN A GROUP

Focusing on "Eat-It-All Elaine" and "Adventures of Isabel"

▶ Talk about what you and your classmates like to eat. Ask your classmates questions about what they say.

▶ Read the titles on page 316 and page 319. Think about what you like to eat.
   • How might the poems be alike?
   • How might they be different?
   • What might happen in each poem?

▶ Get ready to read two poems about two young girls. As you read, think about what the girls eat. Think about what you would add to this chart.

What Elaine Eats	What Isabel Eats

Now turn the page and read "Eat-It-All Elaine" and "Adventures of Isabel." Then you will talk about some unusual eating habits.

Eat-It-All Elaine

A poem by Kaye Starbird

I went away last August
To summer camp in Maine,
And there I met a camper
Called Eat-it-all Elaine.
Although Elaine was quiet,
She liked to cause a stir
By acting out the nickname
Her camp-mates gave to her.

The day of our arrival
At Cabin Number Three
When girls kept coming over
To greet Elaine and me,
She took a piece of paper
And calmly chewed it up,
Then strolled outside the cabin
And ate a buttercup.

Elaine, from that day forward,
Was always in command.
On hikes, she'd eat some birch-bark.
On swims, she'd eat some sand.
At meals, she'd swallow prune-pits
And never have a pain,
While everyone around her
Would giggle, "Oh Elaine!"

One morning, berry-picking,
A bug was in her pail,
And though we thought for certain
Her appetite would fail,
Elaine said, "Hmm, a stinkbug."
And while we murmured, "Ooh,"
She ate her pail of berries
And ate the stinkbug, too.

Pictures by Marie-Louise Gay

317

The night of Final Banquet

When counselors were handing

Awards to different children

Whom they believed outstanding,

To every *thinking* person

At summer camp in Maine

The Most Outstanding Camper

Was Eat-it-all Elaine.

Adventures of Isabel

From the poem by Ogden Nash

Isabel met an enormous bear,
Isabel, Isabel, didn't care.
The bear was hungry, the bear was ravenous,
The bear's big mouth was cruel and cavernous.
The bear said, Isabel, glad to meet you,
How do, Isabel, now I'll eat you!
Isabel, Isabel, didn't worry;
Isabel didn't scream or scurry.
She washed her hands and she straightened her
   hair up,
Then Isabel quietly ate the bear up.

Picture by Susan Jaekel

Think about the poems. Copy the chart on page 315. Fill in the information. Then answer the questions.

1. Use your chart. Also, think about what you know about foods. Which foods in these poems might someone really eat?

2. Do you think these poems tell about real people or make-believe people? How do you know?

3. Why do you think the other campers believe Elaine was the Most Outstanding Camper?

4. Which character eats funnier things? Tell why you think as you do.

5. Pretend that Elaine and Isabel are still hungry. What else might they eat?

6. Why do these poems belong in a unit about unbelievable things?

WORK IN A GROUP

Tell about some unusual foods. Ask questions about what your classmates say. Talk about the unusual foods they suggest.

Focusing on "Sparrow Socks"

▶ Talk about what you know about caring for animals. Ask your classmates questions.

▶ Read the title on page 322. Look at the pictures on pages 322–337. Think about what you know about taking care of animals.
  • What do you think is going on?
  • Do you think the birds like the boy? How do you know?

▶ Get ready to read a story about a young boy and some sparrows. As you read, think about what their problems are and what to add to this chart.

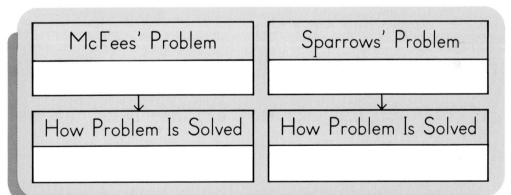

McFees' Problem	Sparrows' Problem
How Problem Is Solved	How Problem Is Solved

Now turn the page and read "Sparrow Socks." Then you will talk about a way to advertise.

Sparrow Socks

A story by George Selden
Pictures by Dan Siculan

Years ago, in a town in Scotland, there lived a little boy whose name was Angus McFee. He lived with his father, Fergus McFee, and his mother, Fiona McFee, and his two uncles, Murdoch and Hamish McFee, in a rambly house at the end of a winding old street.

There was a big garden behind the house. And high in the branches of all the trees many sparrows had their nests. When it was summer, they chirped in the sunlight and fluffed their feathers in the breeze.

But when autumn came, and the chill wind blew, they huddled down in their nests and their bills chattered.

The name of one of these sparrows was Bruce, and Bruce Sparrow was a good friend of Angus McFee.

Angus always made sure that Bruce had plenty of seeds to eat. And in warm weather he kept the birdbath full of water. Bruce and all the other sparrows liked to take a bath every day.

Angus and Bruce played tricks together sometimes too. Bruce could fly upside down and he could hide in Angus's pocket and he could stand on his head in Angus's hand. All curled up inside his feathers, he felt to Angus like a wee puff ball with a heartbeat inside it.

But there wasn't very much time for playing tricks. Every afternoon Angus had to go and help his father and his uncles in their work.

Fergus and Murdoch and Hamish McFee owned a factory that made socks. They had built a wonderful sock machine that clicked and that clacked, and that purred and that whirred. It could make long socks and short socks, and big socks and little socks, and white socks and colored socks, and summer socks and winter socks, and socks with circles on them and socks with squares on them. The wonderful sock machine could make every kind of sock in the whole world!

It was Angus's job to oil all the wheels on the wonderful sock machine and to sweep up the bits of yarn and thread that were left over at the end of each day. Angus loved his job.

But lately he had grown very worried. For the wonderful sock machine worked less and less.

The McFee brothers had only a little factory, with their own little store in front.

It was way off in a corner of the town where the streets were narrow and winding and old. Most people bought their socks from the big stores down in the center of town. And the big stores got their socks from factories all over Scotland.

Every morning Fergus McFee would
meet with his two brothers. They sat at a
long table in the sock factory, and they
thought about socks. And they talked about
socks. And they worried about socks! And
they almost went out of their *minds* about
socks! But they couldn't think how to sell
their socks.

"What we mun have is a beauteous new
sock to sell," said Fergus McFee. "A warm
and woolly winter sock!"

"Ay!" said Hamish and Murdoch
McFee together.

They set the wheels on the wonderful sock machine and put yarn into it. And it clicked and it clacked, and it purred and it whirred. And in a minute out came a beauteous new, warm and woolly winter sock with stripes and a bright red toe on it.

"Weel, 'tis verra pretty!" said Fergus McFee. "Now we mun hope that when cold days come, everybody will buy our socks."

"Ay, let's hope so!" said Hamish and Murdoch McFee together.

The cold days came and the chill wind blew, but everybody went to the big stores to buy their winter socks. And the wonderful sock machine worked less and less.

One morning Angus went out into the garden. Bruce Sparrow was standing on the rim of the birdbath, shivering. Overnight the water had turned to ice. He lifted first one foot and then the other.

"Are your feet cold?" said Angus. Bruce gave a chilly little chirp, and his bill chattered.

"Do you know what I think?" said Angus. "I think you need a pair of socks!" Bruce Sparrow chirped again—happily this time.

That afternoon in the sock factory, when his father and his uncles had gone home, Angus opened the pocket of his jacket. Who should be hiding there but Bruce Sparrow! "It willna take much yarn to make you a wee pair of socks," said Angus.

He set the wheels on the wonderful sock machine so it would make the smallest pair of socks it could. It clicked and it clacked, and it purred and it whirred—and in a minute out popped the tiniest wee pair of socks in the whole world! It was the beauteous new, warm and woolly winter sock with the stripes and the bright red toe on it, but small enough for a little bird to wear.

Angus slipped the socks on Bruce Sparrow's feet. And they fitted perfectly!

Bruce was so happy with his new socks that he jumped up into the air and flew upside down all around the room.

The next morning Bruce Sparrow flew from tree to tree in the garden.

"See my new socks!" he chirped to all the other sparrows. They stood on the cold branches, shivering—first on one foot, then on the other—and their bills chattered.

"We mun have socks too!" they all chirped.

That afternoon Angus was sweeping up in the sock factory. There were only a few bits of yarn and thread left over today, for the wonderful sock machine hardly worked at all. Suddenly a tap-tap-tapping sounded at the window. Angus opened it, and in flew Bruce Sparrow—with his socks on! Behind him came another sparrow, whose bill was chattering.

Bruce Sparrow chirped to introduce his friend.

And the other sparrow gave a chilly little chirp which meant "Please!"

"Oh, I see!" said Angus. "You want a wee pair of socks too."

He set the wheels on the wonderful sock machine, and in a minute the second sparrow had his own pair of socks too.

But then Angus happened to notice that up on the windowsill there was *another* little sparrow whose bill was chattering! He blinked at Angus and gave a chilly little chirp.

And when that sparrow had his own wee pair of socks, *another* one flew in! And then another! And another! And another!

Angus kept saying, "Oh, all right!" and "I guess it's all right!" and "Just one more now!" But before he knew it, he had made socks for *all* the sparrows! He couldn't say no to any bird whose bill was chattering and who gave a chilly little chirp which meant "Please!"

When they all had their new socks, the sparrows gave a big happy chirp which meant "Thank you, Angus!" Then they flew away home to their nests for the night.

Angus finished sweeping up the sock factory. He carefully oiled all the wheels on the wonderful sock machine. And he hoped that somehow it could go on working. And he went home too.

The next day was the strangest day that ever dawned in the town where Angus lived. People looked out of their windows and they saw sparrows everywhere—all wearing little pairs of beauteous new, warm and woolly winter socks with stripes and bright red toes on them!

One lady saw a sparrow pecking for seeds—with his socks on!

A man saw a sparrow pulling up a worm—with his socks on!

A little girl saw a sparrow just going for a walk on the limb of an old oak tree—with his socks on!

Everyone wanted to know where the sparrows got their socks. In a crowd they ran from one big store to another. But the owners of the big stores all said, "No, we dinna sell socks to sparrows here!"

The same morning Fergus and Hamish and Murdoch McFee went to the sock factory as usual. But they found that all their yarn had disappeared! The whole day long they hunted under tables and in closets and all around the sock factory for the yarn. They were so busy hunting that they didn't see any of the sparrows.

In the afternoon Angus arrived with Bruce Sparrow riding in his pocket. He found his father and his uncles sitting at the long table with gloomy faces.

"Someone has stolen our yarn," his father said. "It's all gone!"

"Oh, dear," said Angus. "It mun be the socks I made for the sparrows!"

"You made socks for *whom?*" said his father and his uncles all at once.

Angus told them what he had done. "They were all so verra cold," he explained.

His father only shook his head. "Weel, the yarn's gone now," he sighed.

Bruce Sparrow heard all that was said. He crept out of Angus's pocket, and when no one was looking, he flew out the window.

From tree to tree he went, until he had gathered all the sparrows together.

"We mun give back our socks," he chirped. "Angus used up all the yarn."

"But we dinna *want* to give back our socks!" the sparrows chirped. "We *like* our socks!"

"Ay," said Bruce, "but we got Angus in trouble. So we mun give them back. Everybody follow me."

In a long line all the sparrows flew to the sock factory, in through the window and down onto the table. Then they all began to take their socks off. It was hard work, with only wings to work with, but they pulled with their bills and finally got all their socks off.

Angus and his father and his uncles were amazed! They just stood back and watched.

When their socks were off, the sparrows piled them up in a neat pile on the table. They all gave a big chirp together, which meant "Thanks anyway!"

Just then there came a loud knock-knock-knocking at the door. Angus opened it, and a crowd of people rushed in.

"There are the sparrows and there are their socks!" they all shouted, and they gazed in wonder.

It was the first time this many people had ever been in the sock factory. As long as they all were there, Angus just thought he would ask them something.

"Wouldna all you people like some beauteous new, warm and woolly winter socks with stripes and bright red toes on them?" he said. "We could make them just like the sparrows' socks but big enough for people."

At first no one said anything. Then a wee voice at the back of the crowd said, "Mother, I mun have a pair of Sparrow Socks!"

And another wee voice said, "Mother, so mun I!"

And then everyone began to shout at once.

"Socks!"

"Socks!"

"SOCKS!"

"We all mun have our Sparrow Socks!"

Well, the McFee brothers had never had so many customers in their lives. "Angus," said his father, "give all the sparrows back their socks! They deserve them!" Then Fergus sent Hamish and Murdoch running off to buy more yarn.

Angus slipped their socks back on the sparrows' feet. And while everyone was waiting for the yarn, the sparrows marched around the long table in a sparrow parade— with their socks on!

And now the wonderful sock machine goes click and goes clack, and it purrs and it whirrs all day long!

For all the people in that town—and the dogs and cats too—are wearing their own pairs of beauteous new, warm and woolly Sparrow Socks with stripes and bright red toes on them!

Think about the story. Copy the chart on page 321. Fill in the information. Then answer the questions.

1. Use your chart. What problem do the McFee brothers have? Why is it a problem?

2. When Angus helps the sparrows, he makes a new problem for the McFee brothers. What problem does he cause? How is the problem solved?

3. How might the story be different if Angus had not made the socks for the sparrows?

4. Do you think making a good product is enough to be successful in business? Tell why you think as you do.

5. Why does this story belong in a unit about unbelievable things?

6. Pretend you make socks. How would you advertise them? Tell why.

**WORK IN
A GROUP**

Tell what advertising means to you. Ask questions about what your classmates say. Talk about the answers.

Focusing on "The Big Wind of '34"

▶ Talk about a large object you have seen
blown about by the wind. Ask questions.

▶ Read the title and the introduction on page
341. Look at the picture on page 340. Think
about what you know about the wind.

  • What is the weather like? Tell why you
    think as you do.
  • Will this be a real or a make-believe
    story? How do you know?

▶ Get ready to read a tall tale about a
windstorm. As you read, notice what the
wind does. Think about what you would add
to this chart.

What the Wind Does	
First Next Then Last	

Now turn the page and read "The Big Wind
of '34." Then you will talk about a funny windstorm.

The Big Wind of '34

A tall tale by James Flora
Pictures by Marie-Louise Gay

*If you stay around Grandpa long enough,
you will hear all sorts of amazing stories
about his farm. Some people might call them
tall tales, but you can decide for yourself
after reading this tale as Grandpa tells it.*

When Grandma and I first came to the
farm, there was no barn—just a house. We
were very poor and couldn't afford to build
a barn. We had a cow, and she had to sleep
outside. She didn't like that at all. On cold
days she would get so angry that she
wouldn't give us any milk.

341

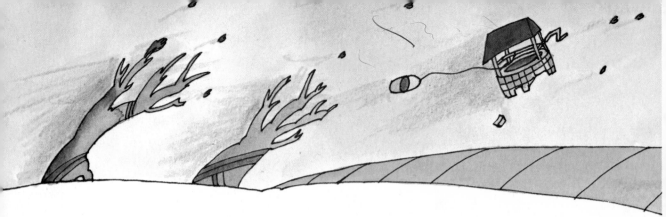

We tried to explain to the cow how sorry we were, but she wouldn't listen. When a cow gets good and mad, she just won't listen to anybody.

Then one day in 1934 the wind started to blow. Oh, my! How it did blow! Harder and harder until it blew all the leaves off the trees. Stronger and stronger until it blew the trees away, too. I had to tie down the cow or she would have been carried away. Even so, she sailed around in the sky like a big cow kite.

I've never seen such a strong wind in my whole life. I had just finished digging a deep well in the backyard. I had to dig it down forty feet, and that was hard work. But that wind huffed and puffed until it blew the well right out of the ground and carried it away. I never did see it again.

That made me so mad that I ran out of the house and threw a big chunk of firewood at the wind. It must have hurt him. It must have made him stop and think how mean he was being to Grandma and me, because the next thing I saw was a big blue barn sailing through the air. It swished over the house and settled there where you see it now. It was a good barn, but it didn't have any doors. So I shouted:

"HEY, WIND! YOU FORGOT THE DOORS!"

That old wind turned right around and
blew back to wherever he had come from.
In no time at all, I could hear him coming
back. Sure enough, he had the doors for
the barn. And he even fetched the pigeon
house you see on top.

When the wind had gone, I went out
and looked around that fine barn. It was
just what I wanted. The only trouble was
that it had settled on our cow's tail and
broken it off. That made me very sad, but
Grandma said not to worry. She said she
had cow salve that would fix everything.
But that's another story, which I will tell
you some day.

Think about the tall tale. Copy the chart on page 339. Fill in the information. Then answer the questions.

1. Use your chart. What does the wind do that is believable?

2. Use your chart. What does the wind do that makes the story unbelievable?

3. Do you think the Big Wind of '34 is a bad wind or a good wind? Tell why you think as you do.

4. How does the writer make the wind seem like a person? Why does he do this?

5. Think back to the poems "Eat-It-All Elaine" and "Adventures of Isabel." Is the character of Elaine, Isabel, or the Big Wind of '34 the most amazing? Why?

6. What do you think is the funniest thing in this tall tale?

7. Why does this story belong in a unit about unbelievable things?

Describe other amazing things the wind might do in this tall tale. Ask questions about what your classmates say. Talk about the answers.

WORK IN A GROUP

Focusing on "Wind Power"

▶ Quickly write everything you know about the wind and what it does. Talk about what you wrote. Ask your classmates about their writing.

▶ Read the title on page 348. Look at the pictures on pages 348–352. Think about what you know about the wind.

- Do you think good or bad things are happening? Tell why you think as you do.
- What might you learn in this story?

▶ Get ready to read an information story about the wind and its power. As you read, think about the harmful and helpful powers of the wind. Copy this chart and take notes.

Harmful Wind Power	Helpful Wind Power

Now turn the page and read "Wind Power."
Then you will talk about the power of the wind.

Connections

Wind Power

On a windy day, the wind pushes against you. You hear it groan and howl. The wind is like an invisible giant. You cannot see the wind, but it has great and surprising power.

The Wild Wind

Wind power sometimes does strange things. Here are some of them.

- A strong north wind blew down the Rhone Valley in France. It picked up rocks and hurled them through windows.
- The north wind once pushed a string of railroad cars twenty-five miles before the cars could be stopped.

Pictures by Jack Wallen

- During a tornado, wind drove a wheat straw into an oak tree.
- In 1928 hurricane winds hit Lake Okeechobee (OH·kee·CHOH·bee) in Florida. The winds blew the lake's waters onto its shore. That was about eight billion tons of water!
- Windstorms have scooped up ponds, then dropped them somewhere else. People are surprised to see it "rain" fish and frogs.

- In 1937 a tornado picked up a train locomotive. It plunked the locomotive down, facing the other way, on another railroad track.
- In Kansas a tornado picked up a long barbed-wire fence. Then it rolled the fence up neatly before dropping it.

Using Wind Power

Wind power can be harmful, but it can be helpful, too. Thousands of years ago someone hung the first sail on a boat. People have been using wind power ever since. For centuries, wind was the main way of moving boats across the seas and oceans of the world.

Today most ships are powered by engines that burn fuel. Fuel is expensive, however, so some ship builders have tried going back to wind power.

Jacques-Yves Cousteau (zhahk•EEV koo•STOH) is an ocean explorer. He has a boat that is powered by the wind. A tall tube, with a flap along its side, is the boat's "sail." A computer turns the flap to catch the wind.

351

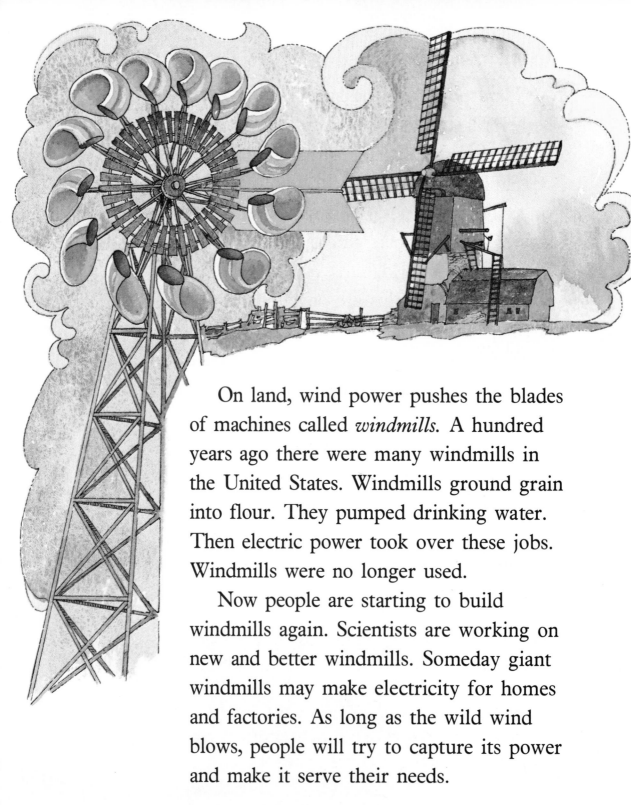

On land, wind power pushes the blades of machines called *windmills*. A hundred years ago there were many windmills in the United States. Windmills ground grain into flour. They pumped drinking water. Then electric power took over these jobs. Windmills were no longer used.

Now people are starting to build windmills again. Scientists are working on new and better windmills. Someday giant windmills may make electricity for homes and factories. As long as the wild wind blows, people will try to capture its power and make it serve their needs.

Think about the information story. Read over the notes on your chart. Then answer the questions.

1. Use your chart. Think about the examples. How can wind power be harmful?

2. Name some kinds of harmful windstorms. Why are they harmful?

3. Use your chart. Think about the examples. Tell how wind power can be helpful.

4. Why do many sailboats have engines as well as sails?

5. Tell why windmills were replaced. Why are people starting to build them again?

6. You have probably flown a kite or held a pinwheel in a breeze. Invent a new toy that uses wind power. Tell about your invention.

7. The facts in this story are true. Why is this selection in a unit about unbelievable things?

Tell how the helpful power of the wind affects your life. Ask questions about what your classmates say. Talk about the answers.

WORK IN A GROUP

TALKING ABOUT THE SELECTIONS

You have read these selections.

Talk
Eat-It-All Elaine *and* **Adventures of Isabel**
Sparrow Socks
The Big Wind of '34
Wind Power

Talk about the selections. Talk about how the ideas and characters are alike and different. Talk about the theme.

1. In which selection are unbelievable things true?

2. What do you think might happen if Elaine and Isabel meet the talking dog and the talking objects in "Talk"?

3. How are the talking things in "Talk" and the Big Wind of '34 alike? How are they different?

4. Which selection tells about the most unbelievable thing? Why do you think as you do?

BOOKSHELF

Best Friends, poems selected by Lee Bennett Hopkins. Harper & Row, 1986. Friends share many wonderful adventures in these poems.

Always Room for One More by Sorche Nic Leodhas. Holt, Rinehart & Winston, 1965. A man with ten children takes in so many travelers that his house falls down.

The Adventures of Spider retold by Joyce Cooper Arkhurst. Little, Brown, 1964. "How Spider Got a Thin Waist" and the other stories in this book tell about the adventures of clever Spider.

Five Sparrows: A Japanese Folktale adapted by Patricia Montgomery Newton. Atheneum, 1982. A Japanese woman helps a hurt sparrow. She is rewarded with a gift of a seed that produces an unending supply of rice.

The Stars in the Sky by Joseph Jacobs. Farrar, Straus & Giroux, 1979. A young girl dreams about wanting stars as toys.

6 There Is a Season...

TALKING ABOUT THE THEME

Look at the picture on pages 356 and 357. Read the title.

1. What is happening in the picture?

2. How can you tell what season it is?

3. What is different about each season where you live?

4. Do you like the changes of the seasons? Tell why you think as you do.

5. You will read some selections. How do you think the selections will be alike?

Other Books About the Seasons

The Sky Is Full of Song, poems selected by Lee Bennett Hopkins. Harper & Row, 1983. See if these poems help you decide which season you like best.

A Circle of Seasons by Myra Cohn Livingston. Holiday House, 1982. One poem, in thirteen stanzas, follows the seasons from spring to spring again.

Focusing on
Poems About the Seasons

▶ Think about your favorite season. Quickly write everything that comes into your mind. Share your writing with your classmates. Ask questions about what your classmates wrote.

▶ Look at the pictures on pages 360–367. Remember what you know about seasons.
  • What seasons will these poems be about? Explain why you think so.
  • Which poems will be about holidays?

▶ Get ready to read poems about the seasons. As you read, notice what details each writer gives. Think about how you would fill in this chart.

Poem Title	Season	Details

Now turn the page and read poems about the seasons. Then you will talk about them.

Winter Night

A poem by Harry Behn

It is very dark
But not late.
Not after eight.

The only light
Comes from snow
Beginning to show.

Bushes are first
As flakes fall,
Then the top of a wall.

What used to be dark
Is now a hill.
It is very still.

Picture by Christa Kieffer

A very fat snowman named Wheezer
Was truly a clever old geezer.
    Whenever he felt
    He was starting to melt,
He'd spend a few days in the freezer.

A limerick by Edward Mullins

Picture by Ed Taber

Winter Walk

A poem by Robert Froman

Cold sky, cold air, cold sidewalk, cold street.

Cold.

SHIVERS.

GOOSE pimples.

RUUUBBB HAAANDDDS.

STAMP FEET.

STILL COLD.

GO IN THIS STORE A MINUTE.

AHHHHHHHH!

In Time of Silver Rain

A poem by Langston Hughes

In time of silver rain
The earth
Puts forth new life again,
Green grasses grow
And flowers lift their heads,
And over all the plain
The wonder spreads
Of life, of life, of life!

March

A poem by Elizabeth Coatsworth

A blue day,
a blue jay
and a good beginning.

One crow
melting snow—
spring's winning!

Spring

A poem by Karla Kuskin

I'm shouting
I'm singing
I'm swinging through trees
I'm winging skyhigh
With the buzzing black bees.
I'm the sun
I'm the moon
I'm the dew on the rose.
I'm a rabbit
Whose habit
Is twitching his nose.
I'm lively
I'm lovely
I'm kicking my heels.
I'm crying "Come dance"
To the fresh water eels.
I'm racing through meadows
Without any coat
I'm a gamboling lamb
I'm a light leaping goat.
I'm a bud
I'm a bloom
I'm a dove on the wing.
I'm running on rooftops
And welcoming spring!

Picture by Christa Kieffer

363

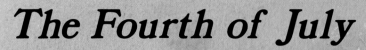

The Fourth of July

A poem by Myra Cohn Livingston

O say
can you
see
in the sky
the rockets
and
pinwheels
zip
by
to
splutter
and flare
as they
sizzle
in
air
and
EXPLODE
on
the Fourth
of
July!

Gently, gently, the wind blows
dandelions' parachutes
into the afternoon sun.

A poem by Kazue Mizumura

Pictures by Christa Kieffer

Fall

A haiku by Sally Andresen

The geese flying south
In a row long and V-shaped
Pulling in winter.

Spendthrift

A poem by Norma Farber

Coins—coins—coins—
    a bushel to a breeze—
are pouring from the pockets
    of the elm in the square.

Gather up the money heaps
    as many as you please.
So rich an old tree
    doesn't count them or care.

Theme in Yellow

A poem by Carl Sandburg

I spot the hills
With yellow balls in autumn.
I light the prairie cornfields
Orange and tawny gold clusters
And I am called pumpkins.
On the last of October
When dusk is fallen
Children join hands
And circle round me
Singing ghost songs
And love to the harvest moon;
I am a jack-o'-lantern
With terrible teeth
And the children know
I am fooling.

Pictures by Christa Kieffer

Think about the poems. Copy the chart on page 359. Fill in the information. Then answer the questions.

page 359.

Think and Discuss

1. Use your chart. How is fall different from winter?

2. Look at your chart. Which season is a time of new beginnings? What details in the poems make you feel this?

3. Do these poems describe winter where you live? If so, tell what details you might add. If not, give details that describe your winter.

4. If you could change the season of summer, what changes would you make?

5. Which poem do you think best belongs in a unit about a season? Why?

6. Think how the seasons change where you live. In what months do they begin to change? What changes take place?

WORK IN A GROUP

Tell what month you like best. Ask your classmates what months are their favorites. Compare your answers. Talk about reasons.

Focusing on "The Four Seasons"

▶ Many changes take place in a year. Talk about the changes in plants and in weather. Ask your classmates questions.

▶ Look at the title on page 370 and the pictures on pages 370–376. Think about what you know about the seasons.
- What facts might this story give?
- Which seasons will the story tell about?

▶ Get ready to read about the changing seasons in a forest. As you read, notice what happens during each season. Take notes on a drawing like this one. Add as many circles as you need.

Spring
Summer
Forest
Winter
Fall

Now turn the page and read "The Four Seasons." Then you will talk about the seasons.

Connections

The Four Seasons

Spring, summer, fall, winter—each season brings its own beauty. Each brings changes to the world of nature.

Why Do We Have Seasons?

The Earth moves around the Sun. This trip takes a year. Look at the picture on page 371. It shows the Earth as each season begins in the northern half of the planet.

The Earth is tilted as it travels. This tilt causes the seasons. In summer the tilt causes more sunlight to reach the northern half of Earth. As the Earth moves on, less sunlight reaches this half of Earth and it is fall. Look at what happens in winter and spring as the Earth continues to move around the Sun.

Pictures by Keith Freeman

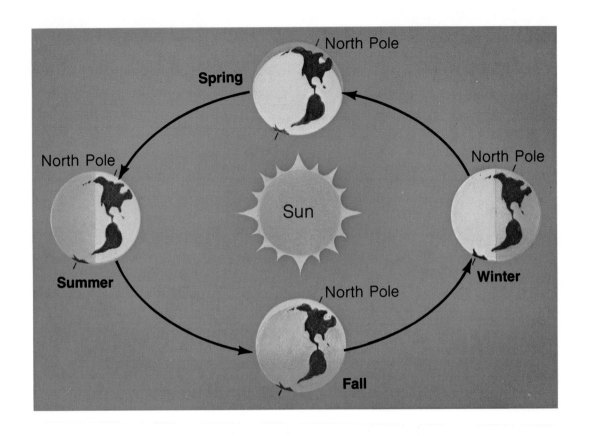

What Changes Do the Seasons Bring?

Each season brings changes to life on Earth. Such changes are easy to see in a *temperate* (TEM·per·it) *forest*. This kind of forest has many trees that lose their leaves in the fall. The temperate forest is the *habitat* (HAB·uh·tat), or living place, for many creatures. The forest changes in many ways as the seasons change.

Spring It is spring in the forest. Sunlight streams through budding branches. It warms the earth. Wildflowers carpet the forest floor. Underground, earthworms tunnel upward, just in time for the return of robins from the south. Everywhere the songs of birds fill the air.

The trees begin to unfold new leaves. Animals and insects awake from a long winter's sleep. Now the animals will begin to shed their winter coats.

Spring is the time for animals to be born. Soon the forest fills with new life. Safe in their nest, these baby squirrels wait for mother to return. They are hungry!

Summer Then summer comes. The forest is hot. It is dark with shade. The animals and birds are quiet. Many of them rest during the day. They come out at night when it is cooler. Summer is the season for insects. They are everywhere, searching for food. Some find it in the trees, where they chew the leaves and rob the trees of sap.

The young squirrels are growing. The older squirrels are still shedding their long hairs. Their tails look thin and ragged. Soon they will begin to grow thick winter coats.

Fall The days are getting shorter and cooler. It is fall. The trees blaze with color. The forest is lit with red, gold, and bright orange. The trees drop their seeds on the forest floor—acorns, beechnuts, hickory nuts, butternuts. These are taken away by birds and animals, to be stored as winter food.

Raccoons and bears eat greedily. They make themselves fat. They will live off this fat in the winter, when food is scarce. Flocks of birds circle overhead. They begin their long flight south.

To prepare for winter, the squirrels now have thick fur coats and bushy tails. They are busy hiding nuts. They bury bushels of nuts over the forest floor. Some nuts will be dug up and eaten. Others will be forgotten, and some will sprout and grow up to be trees.

Winter Fall ends and winter begins. The trees have lost their leaves, and cold snow blankets their branches. Deer search for tender twigs not covered by the snow. Foxes look for rabbits.

Brown bears are curled up, asleep in their caves. Many animals *hibernate* (HY·buhr·NAYT), or spend the winter in a still, quiet state that is almost like sleeping. Below ground, toads, snakes, turtles, and chipmunks hibernate in holes they have made. Insects hibernate, too, protected from the cold by leaves and earth. Other insects have died, but they have left eggs that will hatch in the spring.

On warm winter days the squirrels scamper about looking for food. On cold days they find a hollow tree or nest of leaves and sleep.

The whole forest seems to wait. Soon spring will come, and the circle of the seasons will continue again.

Think about the information story. Look at the drawing you made. Then answer the questions.

1. Use your drawing. Tell how squirrels' lives change during the seasons.

2. Look at the picture on page 371. When the northern half of Earth is tilted away from the sun, what season is it?

3. Use your drawing. Think about the changes plants go through during the seasons. Tell how the changes in plants cause changes in what animals do.

4. Suppose the writer had chosen to describe a city instead of a forest. How would this story have been different?

5. Why is this story in a unit about seasons?

6. Suppose you lived near a forest like the one in the story. Which season would be your favorite? Tell why.

7. Choose a season. Tell how the season makes you feel and why.

Think and Discuss

WORK IN A GROUP

Talk about what you like about the changing seasons. Ask questions about what your classmates say. Discuss their answers.

Focusing on "Panda"

▶ Talk about the needs of newborn babies and animals. Ask questions.

▶ Turn to page 380 and read the title. Then look at the pictures on pages 380–386. Think about what you know about the needs of newborn babies.

  • In what seasons might the events take place? How do you know?
  • What might the baby have to learn?

▶ Get ready to read about a baby panda. As you read, think about the order in which things happen. Think about what you would add to this time line.

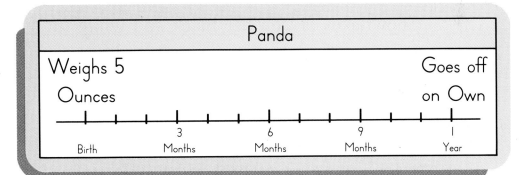

Now turn the page and read "Panda." Then you will talk about how pandas live.

Panda

From the story by Susan Bonners
Pictures by Tom Dunnington

In a mountain forest of southwestern China, a giant panda sits in a birch tree. Snowflakes fall on her black and white fur, but she does not look for shelter. She has lived in snow most of her life.

Early one autumn, the panda found a den in a rocky mountainside. There she made a nest out of broken bamboo stalks. While frosty winds blew through the forest, she gave birth to her cub.

The panda cub was so tiny, she could easily be covered by one of her mother's paws. The cub weighed only five ounces. She was smaller than a kitten, but she had a loud voice that sounded like a baby's cry.

The cub had just a thin covering of white fur. Only her mother's warmth kept her alive. Day and night, the mother panda held her cub tightly against her large, warm body. She never put her cub down.

For several days, the mother panda stayed in the den and nursed her cub. Eventually, the mother had to eat. Carefully, she looked outside. She sniffed the chilly air. She listened to the sounds of the forest. Then, carrying her cub in one paw, the mother panda left the den. She did not have far to go for food. Still cradling her cub, she ate some of the bamboo that grew all around her.

Soon the panda cub began to look like her mother. By the time the cub was one-month old, she had a soft, thick coat of black and white fur. She could not crawl yet, but she could roll around a little.

Now the mother panda could leave her cub for a short time. Before the mother left, she always put her cub in a hidden place. At the cub's first cry, the mother hurried back to soothe her cub by stroking her with a paw.

The cub grew quickly. At two months, she weighed seven pounds, twenty times more than when she was born. Her voice was softer now, a kind of bleating sound. The mother panda played with the cub, tossing her gently between her paws.

All this time, the cub's eyes had been closed. She lived in a world of sounds and smells. She could hear her mother's heart beating. She could smell her mother and feel her warmth, but she could not see her.

At two-and-a-half months, the cub's eyes opened, and she began to see the world around her. She saw bamboo growing in tall thickets that stayed green all winter. There were spruce, birch, and maple trees. Sometimes, a golden monkey swung on the branches. Birds flew overhead—the titmouse, the nuthatch, and the laughing thrush.

At three months, the cub was able to crawl. Now she could explore the world on her own. Often, while her mother slept, the cub sniffed over everything she could find. The cub did not spend all her time exploring, though. Sometimes, she just played.

In the spring, the cub was five months old and still lived on her mother's milk. She weighed twenty pounds.

One day, while her mother was eating bamboo, the cub nibbled a bamboo leaf. She crunched a thin bamboo shoot with her milk teeth. As her jaws became stronger, she ate bigger and bigger stalks.

Her mother could eat woody stalks of bamboo an inch-and-a-half thick. The mother liked to eat some leaves first. Holding the stalk, she let herself fall slowly backwards.

The mother panda ate twenty pounds of bamboo every day. Giant pandas have special linings in their throats and stomachs to protect them. They can even swallow splinters without being hurt.

Summer came. To escape the heat, the cub and her mother went up to the cool meadows above the forest. In the meadows, they ate irises and crocuses, vines, and tufted grasses. A panda has a special bone in its wrist that works like a thumb, so it can pick things up with a very delicate grasp.

Now the panda cub was able to take care of herself, but she stayed with her mother a while longer. The cub kept growing and getting stronger. When she was a year old, she weighed eighty pounds. Her coat became wiry. She lost her milk teeth and grew large permanent teeth.

Then the cub went off to live on her own.

Think about the story. Copy and complete the time line on page 379. Then answer the questions.

1. Use your time line. Which three senses does a panda use first? What does the panda notice with these senses?

2. Why does a panda need to change during the first year?

3. Why does a panda not begin to eat bamboo as soon as it is born?

4. In what season are pandas born? Suppose a cub were born in early summer. Why might it have trouble surviving?

5. Why does this story belong in a unit about seasons?

6. If you were a baby panda, which season do you think you would like best? Why?

7. What do you think the panda's chances of survival are? Why?

Talk about some things that the panda might have to face to survive during the second year. Ask your classmates questions about what they say. Discuss their answers.

Focusing on "Save the Animals"

▶ Quickly write down everything you know about what animals need to live. Then talk about what you wrote. Ask questions.

▶ Read the title on page 390. Think about what animals need to live.
  • What do you think the title means?
  • What kind of facts might be in this information story?

▶ Get ready to read about some animals in danger. Think about what caused the animals' problem. Think about what people are doing to help. As you read, make notes on a chart like this one.

Problem _____	
Causes	How to Help

Now turn the page and read "Save the Animals." Then you will talk about what it means for an animal to be in danger.

Connections

Save the Animals

For a long time giant pandas have lived on cool mountainsides in China. The mountain forests give them shelter and plenty of bamboo, the special food they need to live.

Many people also live in China, and they must have food, too. So mountainsides that were homes for pandas were turned into farmland. Bamboo forests that were the panda's food were cut down.

With fewer forests, there was not enough room or food for all the pandas. Some pandas starved. Fewer panda babies were born. Time passed, and fewer and fewer pandas survived.

390

Then the giant pandas met a new problem. The bamboo forests began to die!

A bamboo plant dies after it grows flowers and produces seeds. The seeds grow into new plants, but it takes at least three years before the bamboo plants are big enough for pandas to eat.

During the time it takes for bamboo plants to grow big, pandas can starve. So people in China and other countries decided to help. Many people gave money for "Project Panda." Rescue teams brought the starving pandas to places where they could be fed and cared for. These pandas were moved to a *preserve* (prih·ZURV), an area planted with bamboo where the pandas would be safe. All over the world people began to study pandas and to seek ways to help the pandas survive.

Yet giant pandas are only one kind of animal that is in danger of dying off. There are many other *endangered animals*. People are trying to save these animals, too.

ENDANGERED! Sea otter
West Coast of the United States

ENDANGERED! Gorilla
West Africa

ENDANGERED! California condor
California

ENDANGERED!
Galápagos giant tortoise
Galápagos islands

ENDANGERED! Bald eagle
United States and Canada

ENDANGERED! Key deer
Florida Keys

Think about the information story. Look at the facts you wrote on the chart. Then answer the questions.

1. Use your chart. What are two things the giant panda needs to live?

2. Look at your chart. What is "Project Panda"? Why is it important?

3. Do you think the Chinese people should have turned the mountainsides into farmland? Give reasons for your answer.

4. Bamboo trees have always died after producing seeds. Why do you think this is a problem only now?

5. Why does this story belong in a unit about seasons?

6. If you were a panda, where would you prefer to live? Why?

7. What do you think is one reason that the California condor and the bald eagle are endangered?

Tell what you think people can do to help endangered animals. Ask questions about what your classmates say. Talk about the answers.

WORK IN A GROUP

Focusing on "I Go Forth to Move About the Earth"

▶ Think about some animals you have seen. Describe them. What are they like? Ask questions about what your classmates say.

▶ Look at the title and the picture on pages 396 and 397. Think about what animals are like.

- How do you think the title and the picture are connected?
- Do you think this poem will be serious? Tell why or why not.
- What words might the writer use to describe the eagle?

▶ Get ready to read a poem. Notice the animals the writer names. Notice how the animals are described. Think about how you would complete this chart.

Animal	How It Is Described

Now turn the page and read "I Go Forth." Then you will talk about some animal qualities.

I Go Forth to Move About the Earth

A poem by Alonzo Lopez

I go forth to move about the earth.
I go forth as the owl, wise and knowing.
I go forth as the eagle, powerful and bold.
I go forth as the dove, peaceful and gentle.
I go forth to move about the earth
    in wisdom, courage, and peace.

Picture by Kazuhiko Sano

Think about the poem. Copy the chart on page 395. Then answer the questions.

1. Use your chart. What three animals are named in the poem? How are they alike?

2. What words describe the animals? Do you agree with the descriptions? Explain your answer.

3. Why might a person compare himself or herself to an animal?

4. Do you think the writer of this poem might be an American Indian? Tell why or why not.

5. Why might this poem belong in a unit about a season?

6. Think of another bird the writer might have named. What words could describe the bird?

**WORK IN
A GROUP**

Tell which animals have qualities that you like. Ask questions about what your classmates say. Talk about the answers.

You have read these selections.

Poems About the Seasons
The Four Seasons
Panda
Save the Animals
I Go Forth to Move About the Earth

Talk about the selections. Talk about how the ideas and characters are alike and different. Talk about the theme.

1. How are the poems "Winter Night" and "Winter Walk" alike? How are they different?

2. How are the mother panda and the mother squirrel alike? How are they different?

3. How are the poems "In Time of Silver Rain" and "Theme in Yellow" alike and different?

4. Which selection best describes the seasons? Why do you think as you do?

BOOKSHELF

Song to Demeter told by Cynthia and William Birrer. Lothrop, Lee & Shepard, 1987. The ancient Greeks believed that the gods controlled everything on earth. This Greek myth explains the seasons of the year.

Old Sadie and the Christmas Bear by Phyllis Reynolds Naylor. Atheneum, 1984. A bear, instead of sleeping through the winter, wakes to take a walk at Christmas. He visits a lady and makes her holiday a special one.

Ox-Cart Man by Donald Hall and illustrated by Barbara Cooney. Penguin, 1979. This story follows a New England farmer in the 1800's from the time he sells his goods and belongings to the time he and his family start the cycle of making and growing things all over again.

Little Wild Lion Cub by Anna Michel. Pantheon Books, 1980. Soft drawings show an active little cub and his family during the first two years of his life.

LITERARY TERMS

CHARACTERIZATION

The ways in which writers present and develop characters to make the characters seem real. Here are several ways in which writers can develop their characters.

1. *By telling how the character looks* **"Grandmother Otis stared down at Amelia. Her hands were on her hips. Her eyebrows met in a disapproving *V*."**

2. *By showing the character's words and actions* **"Grandmother Otis tapped her foot. 'Young lady, was all this your idea?' she asked. 'Or did somebody put you up to it?'"**

3. *By telling the character's thoughts and feelings* **"I suppose," she said to herself, for what seemed like the hundredth time, "I suppose I ought to be counting my blessings instead of grumbling."**

4. *By telling what others think of the character* **"Know something?" Amelia smiled. "You're okay."**

5. *By stating something about the character* **"When a cow gets good and mad, she just won't listen to anybody."**

CHARACTERS

The people (or animals) in a story, poem, or play. Sometimes writers want their story characters to seem real. How the characters think, feel, act, and change are more important than the story's main action, or *plot*. For example, in "Sparrow Socks," author George Selden gives us much information about Angus McFee. We learn what Angus thinks and feels and how he acts. The story is *about Angus*, not just about things that happen in his life. Other stories, such as "Amelia's Roller Coaster," are built mainly around the plot.

DIALOGUE *Conversation between or among characters.* Dialogue is used in almost all forms of writing to move the *plot,* or main action, forward and to tell the reader something about the characters. In the play "The Beach," author Tony Johnston uses dialogue to show how Mole and Troll find out what their problem is:

"Storyteller 1: 'It was a big crab. He had been doing the pinching. They looked so silly that he could not help giggling. Mole and Troll chased him, but he ran into a tight hole and giggled for half an hour.'"

These few lines of dialogue help the reader guess the real problem in the play.

Dialogue is especially important in plays, where conversation is the main way to tell the story and to show each character's personality. In the play "Dance of the Animals," Señor Dog and Señor Goat go to a party and discover that they will be eaten for dinner.

"Señor Goat: '*Amigo,* I do not like the look of that fire. Let us go, for this fire is meant for us. No doubt, Señor Lion means to eat us.'"

Through this conversation, the reader learns that Señor Goat is smart enough to guess what Señor Lion's plan is.

FANTASY *A fiction story with made-up characters and plots.* A fantasy may take place in a world much like the one you know. Yet in the "real world" presented in a fantasy story, ordinary people and animals do impossible things. In the fantasy story "Just the Thing for Geraldine," for example, a possum takes singing and sculpting lessons.

Fantasy offers us the chance to wonder *"What if. . .?" What if* you could be three inches tall, or ride a magic carpet, or travel through time?

See also **Fiction.**

FICTION   *A story made up by the writer.* A work of fiction may be *based* on real things that happen, but it always includes made-up (fictional) characters and experiences. A work of fiction may be brief, like a folk tale or a short story. It may also be a book-length story called a **novel.**

FOLK TALE   *A fiction story made up long ago and handed down in written or spoken form.* Many folk tales have no known authors. Though folk tales come from different parts of the world, many characters, plots, and ideas in them are similar. "The Emperor and the Kite" is a Chinese folk tale retold by Jane Yolen. It tells about a tiny princess who saves her father, the Emperor, and wins his respect. *Fairy tales* like the story "Cinderella" are also a kind of folk tale.

NONFICTION   *A true (factual) story; any writing that tells about things as they really happened, or that gives information or facts about something.* One type of nonfiction is the written history of a person's life. When a person writes his or her own life story, it is called an **autobiography.** When someone else writes a person's life story, it is called a **biography.** Other common forms of nonfiction include news reports, travel stories, personal journals and diaries, and articles on science or history.

PLAY *A story that is acted out, usually on a stage, by actors.* In its written form, a play begins with a **cast of characters,** or a list of the people, or sometimes animals, in the play. A play has a *plot,* or action, just like a story. However, a play is meant to be acted out. The characters in a play tell the story through their words, or **dialogue.**

During a play the actors follow **stage directions,** which tell them *how* to act and speak. Stage directions may also describe the **setting,** where the action takes place. Stage directions are usually not read aloud when a play is acted out.

See also **Dialogue.**

PLOT *The action in a story.* When you tell *what happens* in a story, you are talking about the plot. For instance, in the story "Sparrow Socks," by George Selden, the plot tells how Angus, a young boy, helps sparrows to keep warm by making socks for them. As a result, many people see the socks and want to buy them.

The plot is also the writer's overall *plan* of the action—how, when, and why things happen. The writer uses this plan to arrange the action in an interesting and reasonable order. Each happening becomes a link in a chain of events that makes sense and holds the reader's attention.

The most important part of plot is the problem, or **conflict,** that the main character faces. Sometimes a character struggles with nature (as in Miska Miles's story "Mississippi Possum"). Sometimes a character struggles with another character (as in "Rumpelstiltskin").

SETTING *When and where a story takes place.* If you say "Today in the city," you have given the setting (when and where) before describing the action. Authors can choose any time or place as a setting for a story. In the story "Panda," author Susan Bonners gives us a clear picture of where the giant panda lives.

"In a mountain forest of southwestern China, a giant panda sits in a birch tree. Snowflakes fall on her black and white fur, but she does not look for shelter. She has lived in snow most of her life."

The writer does not always give us the setting so directly. Sometimes we figure it out as the story goes along. Most stories include details about where and when the story takes place. Details may first be given about the weather, city, or country before a specific place is named. In the story "Amelia's Roller Coaster" by Barbara Shook Hazen, a barn and a neighboring farm are details that are given. Later, Chicago is named. The reader might think that the setting is on a farm near Chicago.

GLOSSARY

This glossary gives the meanings of unfamiliar words used in the text of this book. The meanings given here define words only the way they are used in the book. You can find other meanings for these words in a dictionary.

The correct pronunciation of each glossary word is given in the special spelling after that word. The sounds used in these spellings are explained in the following Pronunciation Key. Each symbol, or letter, stands for a sound, a sound you can recognize in the words following it. In addition to these sounds, each glossary pronunciation includes marks to show the kind of force, or stress, with which certain syllables are pronounced. A heavy mark, ′, shows that the syllable it follows is given the strongest, or primary, stress, as in cac•ti (kak′•ti). A lighter mark, ′, shows that the syllable it follows is given a secondary, or lighter, stress, as in hab•i•tat (hab′•ə•tat′).

Several abbreviations are used in the glossary: *v.,* verb; *adv.,* adverb; *n.,* noun; *adj.,* adjective; *pl.,* plural.

Pronunciation Key

a	add, map	m	move, seem	u	up, done
ā	ace, rate	n	nice, tin	û(r)	urn, term
â(r)	care, air	ng	ring, song	yo͞o	use, few
ä	palm, father	o	odd, hot	v	vain, eve
b	bat, rub	ō	open, so	w	win, away
ch	check, catch	ô	order, jaw	y	yet, yearn
d	dog, rod	oi	oil, boy	z	zest, muse
e	end, pet	ou	out, now	zh	vision, pleasure
ē	even, tree	o͞o	pool, food	ə	the schwa,
f	fit, half	o͝o	took, full		an unstressed
g	go, log	p	pit, stop		vowel representing
h	hope, hate	r	run, poor		the sound spelled
i	it, give	s	see, pass		a in above
ī	ice, write	sh	sure, rush		e in sicken
j	joy, ledge	t	talk, sit		i in possible
k	cook, take	th	thin, both		o in melon
l	look, rule	th	this, bathe		u in circus

A

a•ca•cia (ə•kā′•shə) *n.* A tree with fronds and yellow flowers that grows in warm places.

ac•cept (ak•sept′) *v.* To take something that someone offers or gives.

al•fal•fa (al•fal′•fə) *n.* A cloverlike plant with purple flowers, grown as food for farm animals.

ap•pli•ca•tion (ap′•lə•kā′•shən) *n.* A form one fills in with personal information when asking for something.

ar•a•besque (ar′•ə•besk′) *n.* A position in ballet in which the dancer balances on one leg, bends the body forward at the hip, and extends one arm forward, while the other arm and leg are extended backward.

a•rach•nid (ə•rak′•nid) *n.* A class of animals without a backbone and having four pairs of legs and a body divided into two parts. Spiders, scorpions, mites, and ticks are *arachnids*.

ar•mored (är′•mərd) *adj.* Having a covering like armor, a strong protective suit worn in battles.

B

ball (bôl) *n.* A dance.

bal•let (ba•lā′) *n.* A kind of dancing that combines certain steps with light, flowing movements such as leaps and turns. Ballet dancers wear special costumes. Some wear toe shoes to help them dance on their toes.

bam•boo (bam•bōō′) *n.* Woody grasses with hollow stems used for buildings, furniture, and tools. The young shoots are used for food.

ban•quet (bang′•kwit) *n.* A fancy dinner.

barbed wire (bärbd wīr) *n.* Twisted wires with sharp points every few inches.

beau•te•ous (byōōt′•ē•əs) *adj.* Beautiful; pleasing.

bee•tle (bēt′•əl) *n.* An insect with four wings, one pair of which forms a hard shell and covers the other pair when not flying.

bleat•ing (blēt′•ing) *adj.* Crying like a sheep or a goat.

bon•y (bō′•nē) *adj.* Made of bone.

bound•a•ry (boun′•də•rē) *n.* A border or separating line.

brew (brōō) *n.* A kind of drink.

bulg•ing (bulj′•ing) *adj.* Swelling.

C
---

cac•ti (kak′•tī) *n., pl.* Desert plants with thick stems and spines.

calm (käm) *adj.* Peaceful.

Ca•na•di•an (kə•nā′•dē•ən) *adj.* A native of Canada, a country north of the United States.

car•go (kär′•gō) *n.* Goods brought on ships, airplanes, and trucks.

car•i•bou (kar′•ə•bōō′) *n.* Wild reindeer.

cav•ern•ous (kav′•ər•nəs) *adj.* Having a deep, hollow area like a cave.

char•ac•ters (kar′•ik•tərs) *n.* People or animals in a play.

chat•ter (chat′•ər) *v.* To make fast clicking noises.

Chi•na (chī′•nə) *n.* A country on the continent of Asia.

chirp (chûrp) *v.* To make a short, sharp sound.

clay (klā) *n.* Earth or mud that can be used for bricks or pottery.

com•mu•ni•ty (kə•myōō′•nə•tē) *n.* A people with common interests living in a certain area.

com•pu•ter (kəm•pyōō′•tər) *n.* An electronic device that can store, get back, and use information.

con•fi•dent•ly (kon′•fə•dənt•lē) *adv.* In a fearless manner.

con•trap•tion (kən•trap′•shən) *n.* A gadget; a thing built in an unusual way.

cour•age (kûr′•ij) *n.* Bravery.

cov•eys (kuv′•ēs) *n.* Small flocks of birds.

cre•o•sote (krē′•ə•sōt′) *n.* A desert shrub found in the southwestern United States.

cringe (krinj) *v.* To draw away from in horror.

croc•o•dile (krok′•ə•dīl′) *n.* A large, thick-skinned reptile that lives in warm, tropical waters.

cus•tom•er (kus′•tə•mər) *n.* A person who buys goods or services.

cy•clone (sī′•klōn) *n.* A whirlwind; a storm that brings rain and high winds that go around in a circle.

D
---

dan•gle (dang′•gəl) *v.* To hang down.

del•i•ca•cies (del′•ə•kə•sēs) *n.* Special foods.

del•i•cate (del′•ə•kit) *adj.* Easily harmed; finely crafted.

den (den) *n.* A cave used by a wild animal as a living area.

de•serve (di•zûrv′) *v.* To be worthy of having a reward.

dis•guise (dis•gīz′) *v.* To hide one's true appearance by putting on a covering or clothes.

ditch (dich) *n.* A long, narrow hole dug in the ground and used for draining land or for bringing water to plants.

drag•on (drag′•ən) *n.* An imaginary animal usually shown with a snake-like tail, huge wings, and claws.

E

e•lec•tric•i•ty (i•lek′•tris′•ə•tē) *n.* Electric current that runs machines.

el•e•phant (el′•ə•fənt) *n.* A jungle animal with a trunk, four legs, and large ears.

em•per•or (em′•pər•ər) *n.* A ruler of an empire.

en•core (än′•kôr) *n.* A request by an audience for a repeat performance.

en•dan•gered (in•dān′•jərd) *adj.* Threatened with loss of life.

e•nor•mous (i•nôr′•məs) *adj.* Unusually large or great.

es•cape (ə•skāp′) *n.* The act of getting away.

ex•pen•sive (ik•spen′•siv) *adj.* Costing a great deal.

ex•plore (ik•splôr′) *v.* To search.

ex•plor•er (ik•splôr′•ər) *n.* A person who travels to new places to search for special things and to learn about the land.

F

fac•to•ry (fak′•tə•rē) *n.* A building where goods are made.

fa•vor•ite (fā′•vər•it) *adj.* Best-liked.

flock (flok) *n.* A group of birds.

flooded (flud′•əd) *v.* Covered or filled with a great deal of water, usually over land not normally covered with water.

ford (fôrd) *n.* A shallow part of a river or other body of water where people can go across.

forth (fôrth) *adv.* Forward.

fu•el (fyoo′•əl) *n.* Material used to make heat or power by burning, such as wood, coal, or oil.

G

gam•bol•ing (gam′•bəl•ing) *v.* Skipping or running about in play.

ga•zelle (gə•zel′) *n.* A small, quick, and graceful African antelope with curved horns.

geese (gēs) *n., pl.* Large birds with long necks that live near bodies of water and that are between swans and ducks in size.

gon•er (gôn′•ər) *n.* Slang for someone who is dying, lost, or beyond hope.

gra•cious (grā′•shəs) *adj.* Full of kindness and courtesy.

grasp (grasp) *v.* To take and hold tightly or firmly.

greed•i•ly (grēd′•ə•lē) *adv.* Wanting all that one can get.

Greek (grēk) *n.* A person from Greece, a country in Europe.

Green•wich (gren′•ich) *n.* The name of several small towns in the United States or of a borough in Greater London.

guin•ea pig (gin′•ē pig) *n.* A small, round-bodied, short-eared animal that is nearly tailless.

H

hab•i•tat (hab′•ə•tat′) *n.* The place where an animal or a plant usually lives and grows.

har•vest (här′•vəst) *n.* The gathering in of food crops.

hatch (hach) *v.* To come out of an egg.

hi•ber•nate (hī′•bər•nāt′) *v.* To spend the winter in a resting and less active state.

hives (hīvz) *n.* A skin disease in which the skin itches and shows patches or bumps of red.

hoarse•ly (hôrs′•lē) *adv.* Making a rough or harsh sound.

hol•low (hol′•ō) *adj.* Empty on the inside.

hur•ri•cane (hər′•ə•kān′) *n.* A serious storm with heavy rains and strong winds that move in a circle at high speeds.

hutch (huch) *n.* An animal pen.

I

In•di•a (in′•dē•ə) *n.* A country in southern Asia.

in•hab•i•tants (in•hab′•ə•tənts) *n.* Persons or animals that live in a particular place.

in•sects (in′•sekts) *n.* Small animals with three body parts, three pairs of legs, and often two pairs of wings.

in•vis•i•ble (in•viz′•ə•bəl) *adj.* Not able to be seen.

in•vite (in•vīt′) *v.* To politely ask someone to do something.

J

jo•ta (hō′•tə) *n.* A Spanish dance.

jug•gling (jug′•ling) *v.* Keeping several things in the air by tossing and catching them.

L

la•bor (lā′•bər) *n.* Work.

lad•ing (lā′•ding) *n.* A cargo or load.

lair (lâr) *n.* A place where a wild animal sleeps.

lev•ee (lev′•ē) *n.* A bank or wall that prevents flooding.

lin•ing (lī′•ning) *n.* An inside covering of something, such as the lining of a coat.

li•quid (lik′•wid) *n.* A watery fluid.

liz•ard (liz′•ərd) *n.* A reptile with four legs.

lo•co•mo•tive (lō′•kə•mō′•tiv) *n.* The engine of a train.

loy•al•ty (loi′•əl•tē) *n.* The state of being faithful to another person or thing.

M

ma•de•moi•selle (mad′•ə•mə•zel′) *n.* French for an unmarried woman or girl. It means the same as *Miss*.

mag•ni•fy•ing glass (mag′•nə•fī′•ing glas) *n.* A lens that makes things appear larger than they are.

mam•mal (mam′•əl) *n.* The highest class of animals, including humans and animals that have skin usually covered by hair.

marshy (mär′•shē) *adj.* Like a marsh; having soft, wet land.

ma•zur•ka (mə•zər′•kə) *n.* A Polish folk dance.

mes•sen•ger (mes′•ən•jər) *n.* A person who goes on errands.

me•ter (mē′•tər) *n.* A unit of length in the metric system that is equal to 39.37 inches.

mi•gra•tions (mī•grā′•shəns) *n.* Yearly trips by an animal group from one living place to another.

mil•ler (mil′•ər) *n.* A person who grinds grain into flour.

mo•las•ses (mə•las′•iz) *n.* A sweet, dark syrup that is made while sugar is being refined.

monk (mungk) *n.* A man who lives in a special religious house called a monastery.

mor•tar (môr′•tər) *n.* A mixture used to seal bricks together.

mur•mur (mər′•mər) *n.* A low, unclear sound.

mutt (mut) *n.* A dog of mixed breeds.

N

nib•ble (nib′•əl) *v.* To eat or chew in small bites.

O

o•blig•ing•ly (ə•blī′•jing•lē) *adv.* Willingly.

o•li•phaunt (ol′•i•fänt) *n.* Elephant.

or•bit (ôr′•bit) *n.* The path of one object around another.

or•ches•tra (ôr′•kəs•trə) *n.* A group of musicians that plays music together.

P

pal•ace (pal′•əs) *n.* A large, stately house where a king or queen might live.

palps (palps) *n.* Jointed parts that help some animals touch things and taste food.

pan•da (pan′•də) Full name, *giant panda. n.* A large black-and-white animal from China that looks like a bear, but is also related to the raccoon family.

Pa•pa•go Indians (pa′•pə•gō) *n.* An American Indian group living in southern Arizona.

par•a•chute (par′•ə•sho͞ot) *n.* Umbrella-shaped material that helps people float safely to the ground when jumping from an airplane.

peace pipe (pēs pīp) *n.* A decorated pipe that some American Indian groups have used in ceremonies.

per•ma•nent (pûr′•mə•nənt) *adj.* Not changing.

pest (pest) *n.* A person who annoys another.

phlox (floks) *n.* An American herb with red, purple, white, or mixed colored flowers.

pinched (pincht) *v.* Squeezed between finger and thumb.

plié (plē•ā′) *n.* A ballet step by a dancer who points the toes outward, bends the knees, and holds the back straight.

pos•sum (pos′•əm) The informal name for *opossum*. *n.* A small animal that usually feeds at night and lives in trees, found in the eastern United States.

prai•rie (prâr′•ē) *n.* A large area of level or rolling grassy land, having few or no trees, especially the plains of the central United States.

pre•serve (pri•zûrv′) *n.* An area where animals are protected.

prod•ucts (prod′•əkts) *n., pl.* Things that are made or grown by a person, such as farm products.

proj•ect (proj′•ekt) *n.* A large task or job.

pro•tect (prə•tekt′) *v.* To keep from harm.

R

rav•en•ous (rav′•ə•nəs) *adj.* Very hungry.

re•as•sur•ing (rē′•ə•shŏŏr′•ing) *v.* Freeing from fear or doubt; giving confidence.

reck•on (rek′•ən) *v.* To plan or count on.

rec•re•a•tion (rek′•rē•ā′•shən) *n.* Play or amusement.

res•cue (res′•kyŏŏ) *v.* To save from danger, harm, or disaster.

riv•er (riv′•ər) *n.* A large, natural stream of water; often fed by smaller streams and flowing to a lake or sea.

roast•ing pit (rō′•sting pit) *n.* A large hole in the ground over which food is cooked.

S

salve (sav) *n.* A sticky medicine to put on wounds and sores.

saw•mill (sô′•mil′) *n.* A place where logs are cut.

scarce (skârs) *adj.* Not plentiful.

sci•en•tist (sī′•ən•tist) *n.* A person who studies science.

Scot•land (skot′•lənd) *n.* A country in Europe north of England and part of the United Kingdom of Great Britain.

sculp•ture (skulp′•chər) *n.* The art of carving or modeling materials into figures or shapes.

sea•weed (sē′•wēd) *n.* Plants that grow in the sea.

set•tler (set′•lər) *n.* A person who moves to a new place that has few or no people.

shal•low (shal′•ō) *adj.* Not deep.

shel•ter (shel′•tər) *n.* Something that covers and protects.

shiu•li (shōō′•lē) *n.* A flower that blooms in the morning.

shiv•er (shiv′•ər) *v.* To shake from being cold.

sieve (siv) *n.* A utensil made of wire mesh or metal with many small holes, used for straining.

sloe (slō) *n.* A small, sharp-tasting, plum-like fruit.

slope (slōp) *n.* Rising or falling ground; a hill.

spar•row (spar′•ō) *n.* A small, singing bird of a dull brown color.

spend•thrift (spend′•thrift′) *n.* A person who spends wastefully.

spi•der (spī′•dər) *n.* A small animal with two body parts, four pairs of walking legs, and no wings.

splin•ter (splin′•tər) *n.* A sliver; a thin piece split off a larger part.

spout (spout) *n.* The opening through which a drink is poured.

square (skwâr) *n.* An open space near the center of a town and bounded by streets on all four sides.

stalk (stôk) *n.* The main part of a plant.

starve (stärv) *v.* To die from hunger.

stool (stōōl) *n.* A backless and armless seat like a king or queen's throne.

stunned (stund) *v.* Made unconscious or unable to act.

sur•vive (sər•vīv′) *v.* To remain alive.

sus•pi•cious (sə•spish′•əs) *adj.* Distrustful; suspecting.

swiv•el chair (swiv′•əl châr) *n.* A chair that turns on its base.

T

tame (tām) *adj.* Not wild.

tan•go (tang′•gō) *n.* A ballroom dance from Latin America.

taunt•ed (tônt′•əd) *v.* Challenged or made fun of in a mocking way.

tem•per•ate (tem′•pər•it) *adj.* Mild.

tem•per•ate for•est (tem′•pər•it fôr′•ist) *n.* A woods where many trees lose their leaves in the fall.

thick•et (thik′•ət) *n.* A thick growth of plants.

thyme (tīm) *n.* A garden herb used in cooking.

tick•er tape pa•rade (tik′•ər tāp pə•rād′) *n.* A traditional hero's welcome in which ribbons of paper are thrown from buildings as the hero passes by.

tide pools (tīd pōōls) *n.* Pools of sea water left by the sea.

tilt (tilt) *v.* To lean or slant. *n.* A leaning position.

tor•na•do (tôr•nā′•dō) *n.* A funnel-shaped cloud of whirling winds that moves over land, destroying anything in its path.

tri•al (trī′•əl) *n.* Test; time during which something is tried out.

tri•umph (trī′•əmf) *n.* Victory.

tum (təm) *Informal.* Short for *tummy.* *n.* Stomach.

tu•tu (tōō•tōō) *n.* A short skirt worn by a ballerina.

U

un•yield•ing (un′•yēl′•ding) *adj.* Firm; steady; unbending.

V

Vic•trol•a (vik•trō′•lə) *n.* A record player.

W

waltz (wôlts) *n.* A ballroom dance.

web (web) *n.* A fine net woven by some spiders to catch food.

wind•mill (wind′•mil′) *n.* A building with sails on a wheel that are turned by the wind.

wiry (wīr′•ē) *adj.* Being thin and able to move easily.

wis•dom (wiz′•dəm) *n.* Good sense; judgment.

wool•ly (wōōl′•ē) *adj.* Like wool from a sheep's coat.

Y

yam (yam) *n.* A root, like a sweet potato, that is eaten.

yarn (yärn) *n.* A string of fiber used for weaving, knitting, or making thread.

Z

zig•zag (zig′•zag) *n.* A series of short, sharp turns or angles.

0
1
2
3
4
I 5
J 6